Practical Building Repairs

Small Works Solutions for Surveyors and Builders

Stuart Hill BSc Hons MRICS FB Eng
with Cost Sequences by
Peter Dyne MRICS,
Building Cost Information Service (BCIS)

Acknowledgements

This book is based on my experiences over the past twenty-five years of maintaining, altering and constructing commercial and domestic buildings.

Many people have helped during the preparation of the book, giving both their time and useful suggestions. In particular I would like to thank John Lanning, Pam Rodham, and Bruce Howse and other staff at calfordseaden llp.

Thanks are due to Peter Dyne MRICS, Technical Consultant for the Building Cost Information Service (BCIS), for the preparation of the costings that enhance the technical chapters; and to Andrew Spelman of Page Bros, for the excellent interpretations of my original line drawings. I should also mention the assistance of Sophie Brooks and Nina Stovold from RICS Books, who both showed considerable patience when chasing down late text! And to Melanie Thompson, for creating the illusion that I have some command of the Queen's English, and for considerable work in checking references.

Of course any book is something of a team effort – and this one is in no small degree due to the support from my family who have given me the time to write it. So it is dedicated to Fiona, Phoebe and Cameron.

Stuart Hill
Clanfield, Hampshire
June 2008

Published by the Royal Institution of Chartered Surveyors
Surveyor Court
Westwood Business Park
Coventry CV4 8JE
UK

www.ricsbooks.com

ISBN 978 1 84219 3778

Typeset and printed in Great Britain by Page Bros

Contents

Introduction

The UK property sector is in the throes of a period of considerable uncertainty. On the one hand we are faced with a serious shortage of supply in the housing sector, particularly in the South East of England; on the other, we see planning delays, skills shortages and the on-going uncertainty of the 2007 'credit crunch'. The commercial property sector faces similar dilemmas.

Add to this the government's obligation to improve the overall standard of all buildings in order to cut energy usage in the wake of international targets designed to curb climate change, and it's easy to see that we're facing very interesting times indeed!

The Europe-wide Energy Performance of Buildings Directive (EPBD) is being phased in over the next three years, and ultimately means that all properties – commercial and domestic – that are sold, and many that are rented, will have to be assessed in terms of their energy efficiency and environmental impact. On the homes front, this will be implemented via the notorious Home Information Pack (HIP), which includes a pre-purchase 'energy performance certificate' of any dwelling put on the market.

Thus the 'Home Inspector' is likely to become a new phenomenon; and the nation's housing stock will be subject to much closer scrutiny than ever before. Equally, householders will be more aware of the implications of maintenance and correct repairs.

Change is not always welcome; but in this case it is certainly inevitable. But do not despair! Though many of us are about to climb a sharp learning curve, all this change is a business opportunity for well-prepared surveying practices.

As well as the need for suitably qualified Home Inspectors, the inspecting regime will mean that householders will be far less able to get away with the permanent 'temporary' repair approach that is currently so common. Prospective purchasers or tenants will be pre-warned about a property's pitfalls and defects.

Where in the past the homeowner could choose the do-it-yourself approach, this is less likely to happen, because fewer people have the time or skills to do their own property maintenance, and for some repairs (e.g. any electrical work) a DIY approach is illegal. Yet it won't be easy to find a suitably qualified tradesperson to do the work; either because the good ones are fully booked for months ahead, or because of concerns over 'cowboys'.

The situation is hardly better in the public rental sector. The massive changes that began in the 1980s, whereby homes that were formerly built and managed by local authorities were transferred to a plethora of housing associations and registered social landlords (RSLs), means there is now a substantial stock of housing in need of repairs and maintenance. But at the same time the trend towards offsite manufacture, and pre-assembled and packaged building components, has had a knock-on effect on the building team's ability to maintain and repair the building stock. Where once a cost-effective repair was made, now it may be tempting to replace a defect with a (more expensive) standard stock component.

Many landlords, homeowners and occupiers will therefore be in need of expert guidance to get their property matters properly addressed. Step forth the surveyor or Home Inspector – suitably qualified and ready to specify and, if necessary, contract-manage a wide range of repairs and minor works. A veritable 'one stop' solution.

And yet...

Of course, this sounds like a wonderful new era for the surveying profession (and in some respects, it is). However, the skills shortage has not only ravaged the 'trades' – these days, when academic qualifications are far more prized than practical skills, we are also facing a lack of suitable skills and hands-on experience in the surveying profession.

And that's where this book steps in.

I have spent more and more time over the last 15 years or so 'inventing' clever repairs as part of a process of repairs and alterations on all types of building (particularly converting old hotels or office buildings into flats). Of course, I have not really invented them – they are an evolution and adaptation of traditional and sometimes rather forgotten repair techniques; but they are still very valid and useful.

By gathering all these various repair techniques together into one handy manual, and liberally scattering my lifetime's experience of wider construction issues – such as tackling the knottier aspects of legislation, and the importance of having a proper contract – I hope to inspire and encourage surveyors (and builders, and their clients) to think differently about how repairs might be achieved, and not to 'replace with new' as a default, without exploring the cheaper, but equally effective, repair options first.

This book provides advice mainly, but not exclusively, in the field of simple traditional buildings; probably residential. But many commercial buildings will share similar characteristics. There is, after all, a considerable overlap between the two; although many books have tended to separate the types of use rather than the types of building.

'Designed' structures – that is to say those with a high degree of engineering input – are largely outside the scope of this book, at least as far as the sections dealing with the main wall and possibly roof fabric are concerned. Nevertheless, many of the repairs and solutions in this book are 'robust'. However, it is important to follow manufacturers' guidance, where appropriate. Overall, use the book to inspire the methodology, but always ensure you have properly scoped the project too.

Throughout the book I have tried to point out where common mistakes get repeated in repairs work, and where these can be easily avoided. I have also tried to lighten the load by adding a number of anecdotes from my own experience – the sorts of memorable stories I often tell to newly qualified surveyors who join our practice. They really did happen; honest.

Overall, the book is designed to be useful to anyone considering repairs, designing extensions or alterations, contracting and specifying small works, or who is generally involved in making buildings 'work' and in giving them a cost-effective new lease of life.

Therefore the information on repairs, new build or extension projects will be relevant to projects worth up to around £200,000 at current values (2007).

Most recently qualified or about-to-qualify surveyors will be more familiar with CAD than the drawing board. Nevertheless, I think drawing is a wonderful habit to practice (however bad the drawings may be). Drawing is a skill that has declined, but which I would urge you to re-discover. With a bit of practice, drawing can become a very quick and effective means of communication whether on site, in the office or with the client. It also helps with analysis of problems – sometimes at a sub-conscious level.

So, whether you are a Building Surveyor (or indeed a 'GP') involved with repairs and small works; or are changing your field of experience and practice, and want to get up to speed; or if you are on the road to qualifying, or are consolidating your experience after just framing your diploma; or indeed want a 'refresher' for repairs ideas – then I hope you will find something in here to help you.

Ideally builders will read the book too – especially trades who have previously tended to specialise in new-build work and may now be looking to diversify into maintenance contracting (for private investment stock or housing association estates for example).

HOW TO USE THIS BOOK

By including sketches and checklists, I hope the book will be an easily thumbed reference, and the Building Cost Information Service (BCIS) pricing for 'typical' repairs – which are all based on cost data from the 4th quarter of 2007 (and exclude Value Added Tax) – should assist with advising clients or checking builders' estimates or quotations.

The language and format are designed to inspire you with new ideas and solutions. Ideally, the book will become a bit dog-eared and stay in your car as an easy reference to help explain your repairs solutions to the client or builder on site.

There are some excellent texts on the market to help practitioners conduct building condition surveys, analyse defects and work out what went wrong, and the introduction of the HIPs for residential properties is likely to extend this. There are a few books that address the repairs issues, although some of the best of these are now a little long in the tooth, and do not always reflect current practice and development of new materials or methods. This book aims to bridge the gap between the two.

There is only one underlying assumption to this book: I have assumed that you, or someone else, has already conducted a building condition survey.

With that in mind, I have not repeated survey methodology here; instead I highlight some potential pitfalls where it could be easy to make some (wrong) assumptions when preparing a condition report – or relying on someone else's – and where some re-consideration may be appropriate when formulating a repair or adaptation solution.

I have imagined that you have been appointed by a client (probably a householder; perhaps the owner of a small business), to advise on repairs following an adverse mortgage valuation or building condition survey, or perhaps following service of a Schedule of Dilapidations on a commercial property (and where the 'other' surveyor is insisting on a rebuild or replacement where a 'tenantable repair' would prove quite sufficient and considerably cheaper). That is, you should have enough information to prepare a simple specification to do the works, get them priced, and set up and oversee a basic form of contract.

The first part of the book – Before you start – examines:

● the statutory/regulatory framework
● aspects of standard surveying administration – the 'paperwork' context of doing the job

i.e. all the things you need to consider before you jump in and advise the client. Although this book is based on my own experience and therefore deals mainly with works that come under the statutory control regime of England and Wales, the basic principles will apply in Scotland (and elsewhere), given a little intelligent application.

The second part of the book – Repairs: problems and solutions – reviews:

● the actual repairs strategies you might apply.

The sequence broadly follows that which you might apply in a condition survey, and I hope this will make it quick and easy to refer to – especially where you may be reviewing someone else's condition report identifying defects by construction element.

Overall, I have set out to look at appropriate and practical techniques for repairs, small extensions and so on, to outline the regulatory framework, and contractual options and look at some of the practical building issues and 'wrinkles'. Along the way I hope it will de-mystify some of the black arts of Building Surveying to the small builder and General Practice Surveyor, and will help with improving a dialogue among members of the building team – on whatever scale it operates.

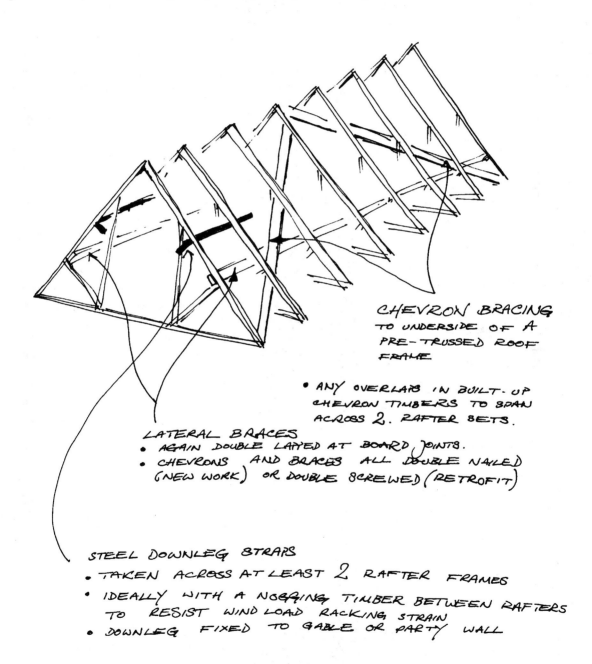

CHEVRON BRACING TO UNDERSIDE OF A PRE-TRUSSED ROOF FRAME

● ANY OVERLAPS IN BUILT-UP CHEVRON TIMBERS TO SPAN ACROSS 2 RAFTER SETS.

LATERAL BRACES
● AGAIN DOUBLE LAPPED AT BOARD JOINTS.
● CHEVRONS AND BRACES ALL DOUBLE NAILED (NEW WORK) OR DOUBLE SCREWED (RETROFIT)

STEEL DOWNLEG STRAPS
● TAKEN ACROSS AT LEAST 2 RAFTER FRAMES
● IDEALLY WITH A NOGGING TIMBER BETWEEN RAFTERS TO RESIST WIND LOAD RACKING STRAIN
● DOWNLEG FIXED TO GABLE OR PARTY WALL

PART 1 – Before you start

Chapter 1
Business matters and job planning

Project Management is a much-abused term and seems to mean all things to all people. So, before getting stuck into a project you need to be quite clear in your own mind exactly what the parameters of the job should be – and your own role in it.

It's not as easy as it sounds; all too often a bit of informal advice to a client evolves into a full blown project. Many professional indemnity (PI) claims result from either the surveyor not accurately defining instructions or, even if they were defined, the client not understanding them properly.

For even the simplest of jobs, you need to ask:

- Will I be responsible for design and specification?
- Will I take care of Contract Administration (and farm-out the design bit if you are not confident to do it, or if parts are quite specialised)?
- Will I will be supervising the works (and all that entails – a much higher level of involvement and responsibility than in Contract Administration)?
- Will I have the power to instruct other consultants (such as structural engineers) on behalf of the client, or will consultants be contracted directly by the client?

All of which needs to be recorded and agreed in writing with the client. Depending on the level of complexity of the project, this may simply be an exchange of letters, or could extend to a full-blown contract (see Chapter 2).

FEES

One thing your letter/contract must certainly discuss is the question of fees.

Generally, an hourly rate will be appropriate. However, domestic projects can soon grow beyond expectations, resulting in fees that are beyond the client's ability to pay.

Often it will be appropriate to have a 'menu' of fees so that the unexpected can be covered with a fee rate in advance. For example, on slightly larger projects (such as an extension or new build works) you may need to liaise with service providers in order to negotiate a sewer or drain diversion, perhaps. (Drains have a nasty habit of appearing in a completely different place from the one shown on the record plan.) Therefore, your fees must make adequate provision for site investigation in advance.

In other words, don't skimp on the preparation stage (a common theme in this book!).

Other considerations include:

- Will fees be invoiced as a percentage of the contractor's periodic billing (usually 14 or 28 days) or at the end of a small job? The contract terms may specify periodic payments, e.g. to coordinate with specific stages in the contract (if you use one of the standard contract forms), so you will need to be clear how this will work in practice.
- Insurance – in relation to contracts, as well as professional indemnity (PI).

INSURANCE

Insurance is something of a paranoia-inducing subject for surveyors, with unhappy experiences of ever-increasing PI insurance premiums year on year!

But whatever your profession or trade, it is essential you consider insurance in the round and not just from a PI stand point.

PI, however, is probably as good a place to start as any. In particular, at the time of writing it is being suggested that the PI cover for HIPs reporting will be on a 'per case' basis rather than the traditional surveyors' annual premium. So we may have to wait and see how the PI market evolves in the near future to reflect this.

Professional indemnity (PI) insurance

If you are a member of a professional body (and I am assuming that many readers will be members of RICS Building Surveying, QS, or General Practice divisions) you should verify the extent of your PI cover and any caveats which may apply to it. For instance, it might restrict those in the practice who are not yet qualified, or who have less than a given number of years of experience from working unsupervised – precluding sending someone out to site for a quick check if there are more onerous implications.

My advice to readers of other professions/trades is likewise: always check the scope and caveats in your PI policy; and if you don't currently have PI, get it! Most professional bodies and trade associations will be able to advise you on the most appropriate policy for the work you undertake; and many will have negotiated discount cover for their members.

Traditional PI products are usually based on the experience of the practice and the percentage/ proportion of the types of work undertaken – valuation work probably attracting the most heavily loaded premiums to reflect the claims risk.

You may find that your 'normal' PI policy does not include cover for structural calculation work, so you should establish exactly how this is specified in the policy. For example, if you subcontract this function to a consultant you may pick up a proportion of the liability (usually in proportion to the fee split which is considered to reflect the apportionment of risk too).

Consequently you may find it more appropriate to get sub-consultants to contract directly with the client for this sort of advice and ensure you do not put yourself in a position of vicarious liability by overly recommending one consultant above another!

Fortunately, claims for engineering consultancy are comparatively rare, but that is no reason to be complacent.

It is essential that you check what cover is available, if you propose to specify and manage building repairs work.

Contract Administration is straightforward and, essentially, so too is Project Management, but insurers may perceive the risks differently, and certainly a Project Manager is likely to have more liabilities based on current interpretations of case law. One of these liabilities is to check that appropriate insurances – for the works – are effected where needed.

Project-specific insurance

Typically the contractor insures 'the works', and if new work is being done to an existing building then the owner or occupier insures the existing building fabric and contents.

At the time of writing the minimum level of third party insurance cover is £2 million.

However, you should carefully consider the options in the contract. Contracts are discussed in detail in Chapter 2, but suffice to say here that not all contracts offer the same options. For example, Section 5 of the JCT Minor Works contract sets out the insurance provisions, giving two alternatives (Clause 5.4a and 5.4b) for insuring 'the works':

- Clause 5.1: establishes the contractor's broad liability for personal injury or death and related loss claims in respect of progress of the works (except of course where the employer has a duty/ responsibility)
- Clause 5.2: likewise establishes the detail of the contractor's liability for injury or damage to third party property but not 'the works'
- Clause 5.3: establishes the contractor's obligation to indemnify the employer for Clauses 5.1 and 5.2 and to take out the appropriate insurance in addition
- Clause 5.4a: sets a duty on the contractor to insure in the joint names of the employer and the contractor the works and site materials for loss or damage to full reinstatement value plus fees
- Clause 5.4b: provides a second option: the employer insures in the joint names of the employer and contractor to cover any existing buildings (and contents).

Although the contractor is required to demonstrate that insurance is in place, the second option is likely to be the most common where improvements or repairs are being made to an existing property.

The most cost-effective option may be for the owner to notify the existing insurers and amend the policy with a 'joint names cover' for the period of the contract.

If you are acting as Contract Administrator you have a duty to tell the employer of their obligations in this regard.

Warn clients about their obligations

It's tempting to think this is overkill, but in my experience, even if the issue only reaches the level of a 'small claim' the costs can soon mount up.

Consider the consequences if, during the course of extending or making repairs to a roof, defective sheeting let in the rain, which caused considerable water damage to the part-completed internal repair/improvement works. Think of the potential damage to personal possessions, or drowned home or office computers and paperwork, plus the consequential losses possible from loss of work or working ability, or the hotel or rental costs of other temporary accommodation while the problem is rectified!

Expecting the unexpected

Sometimes insurance cover for 'additional risks' is appropriate. This is unlikely to be an issue in a small repair scenario, but where there is a new build, or extension works, then archaeological insurance may be a wise investment.

In an old city, or even a village or hamlet where there may be layers of mediaeval, Roman or Saxon developments lurking not too far beneath the surface, the contractor is obliged to bring any archaeological finds to the attention of the local authority's Archaeological Officer. This is frequently a condition of some Planning Permissions as well. On some sites, if antiquities are suspected, then a representative of the local authority may sit-in during the excavation of the foundations or slab and examine the spoil excavated to assess if there is anything of value.

If anything of value is found, all works on site may be suspended to allow for a 'dig' and the site to be fully recorded, sometimes with protective measures to preserve the ground for more detailed investigation when the building site is next recycled.

The cost to the development programme could be enormous.

PROJECT ASSESSMENT CHECKLIST

Early decisions can have wide-ranging implications, so a fundamental aspect of Project Management (whatever your interpretation of that term) is to be prepared for where your decisions and actions are leading you. So it is wise to think carefully before committing yourself (or your client) to any particular strategy.

Set out below is a checklist that is designed to act as a prompt during project assessment and planning. It can also form the basis of an agenda for recording pre-start or site meeting minutes with the client and contractor.

Of course, not all of the headings will apply to all jobs, and it may be too heavy duty for simple one-off repairs. But where you are involved in altering, adapting or extending buildings or building new ones it should give you a point to start from.

- Phase One is intended to follow the desk-top study stage, while all the planning is in hand.
- Phase Two looks at issues once 'feasibility' has been established and design work or specification has been commissioned.
- Phase Three looks ahead to once the work starts, but some of the headings may be useful if reviewed out of sequence.

Project assessment checklist

PHASE 1: Feasibility study and information acquisition and appraisal

Item		Actions/notes
1. General information review	Receipt of trigger notice (or client's initial instructions)	
	Confirm receipt of any paperwork or information relating to location of statutory services such as gas, electricity, water and so on	
	Title information: verify legal aspects 　　Boundaries 　　Title 　　Adopted roads and path	
	Planning use (Use Classes)	
	Frame manufacturer and type (if pre-fabricating); or confirm 'traditional' route	
2. Engineering and planning review and information requirements	Desktop study and briefing notes	
	Digest from similar nearby sites and information transfer/input	
	Historical/anecdotal information from any in-house property database (e.g. title, leases/sub-leases, 'as built' drawings, maintenance data)	
	Previous health and safety file notes/asbestos survey/geology from housing records, the original building records, etc.	
	Topographic reports	

PHASE 1: Feasibility study and information acquisition and appraisal *continued*

Item		Actions/notes
2. Engineering and planning review and information requirements *continued*	Soil/geophysics reports	

	Drainage (existing)
	  Surface water
	  Foul water
	  Highway	

	Asbestos (existing)	
	Eco-survey/Environmental Protection Act 1990 (e.g. any protected species such as bats, or invasive plants such as Japanese Knotweed?)	
	Flood risk assessment	Verify with local authority Verify with Environment Agency
	Disabled access issues	Verify with local authority Verify with Building Control

	Party Wall issues
	  Engineering impact
	  Foundation depths
	  Sub-consultants required? (Collateral Warranties and sub-consultants)	

	Initial preparation of briefing note for architects and core design group	
	Feasibility issues/engineering opinion	
	Any existing/previous Planning Permissions to inform design process?	
	Site constraints	
	Traffic and parking surveys	
	Use Class and any changes to Use Class Order (UCO) category	

	Existing statutory services (check capacity, diversions required etc.)
	  Gas
	  Electrics/cables (pylons/poles/overhead cable; high voltage lines)
	  Drains (foul water; surface water)
	  Water (potable)
	  Telecoms/Cable	

	Archaeological risk Consider insurance/Conservation Area	
	Tree Preservation Orders (TPOs)	
	Any known road widening schemes/development plans	
	Boundary ownership	
	Known soil problems	
	Covenants and restrictions	
	Right to Buy/Buy Back properties which may interfere with site (if within public rented sector)	

PHASE 1: Feasibility study and information acquisition and appraisal *continued*

Item		Actions/notes
3. Planning/Design Strategy Requirements	Review current Employer's Requirements	
	Any specific changes, e.g. for EcoHomes rating?	
	Define which template version is operating, if using standardised designs (social housing only)	
	Advise frame manufacturer accordingly, if using standard timber/steel/concrete off-site manufacture and/or prefabrication	
	Security requirements specific to site?	
	Plans for future nearby expansion/tie-in developments strategically with adjoining sites	
4. Financial	Funding restrictions/timetable	
	Grants, subsidies/tax advantages	

	Budget setting
	    Total internal measurement (in m^2)
	    Basic budget (or agreed £ per m^2)
	    'Abnormals' subject to ringfenced contingency (identify 'fixed' costs and variable 'abnormal' items)
	    Total project budget
	    Agreed maximum price
	    Cash flow	

	Risk register Initial financial risk items to be scheduled within core group minutes	
5. Health and safety issues	Initial risk items	
	Possible design risk items	
	Decant (occupied sites) or special protection	
	Access to adjoining land and buildings	
	Any additional survey advice needed?	
	Traffic movement patterns and planning	
	Vehicle access/plant and restrictions on access	
	Site slope and contours	
	Styles/gates/rights of way	
	Flooding	
	Unsafe trees	
	Properties adjoining site	
	Sensitive neighbours – schools, hospitals, courts etc.	
	Pre Tender Plan	
	Pre Contract Plan	
	F10 Health and safety notification	
	Health and safety file	

PHASE 1: Feasibility study and information acquisition and appraisal *continued*

Item		Actions/notes
6. Programming and target dates for design team	Target practical completion date	
	Target date for frame on site (if prefab)	
	Target start on site date	
	Target frame order date (to achieve delivery on site)	
	Target agreed maximum price (AMP) date	
	Target detailed design date	
	Target Planning Application	
	Target client final approval date	
	Target completion of tenants consultation date	

7. Engineering	Roads and footpaths
	   Stopping up orders
	   Section *[1]
	   Section *
	   Section *
	   Wayleaves/Easements
	   Design	

	Drainage
	   Section *
	   Section *
	   Section *
	   Wayleaves/Easements
	   Design	

	Foundations (design)	
	Supporting structures (design)	
	Structural calculations	
	Environment Agency approvals	

	Services – quotes
	   Gas
	   Electric
	   Telecoms/cable connections
	   Water	

	Services – enquiries
	   Gas
	   Electric
	   Telecoms
	   Water	

[1] Insert here details of any relevant statute (e.g. Highways Act) that needs to be checked or permissions obtained at this stage. (Section agreements may be required for a number of specific actions; see item 8, below.)

PHASE 1: Feasibility study and information acquisition and appraisal *continued*

Item		Actions/notes
8. Section Agreement Schedule and Advice with Section Agreement Progress (Insert extra lines here for each separate Section Agreement listed in item 7).	Aide Memoire and Section Agreement Purpose Person Tasked for Action	Progress/Notes/Target date
9. Handover	'Shared ownership' checklist (social housing)	
	Handover forms	
	Effects forms	
	Tenants pack	
	Phased handover	
	Special requirements	
	Gas and electric certificates	

PHASE 2: Design evolution

Item		Actions/notes

10. Design and Planning	Stage 1 – Design protocol – externals
	    Highways
	    Turning heads
	    Footpaths
	    Drying areas
	    Bin stores
	    Bike stores
	    Fences
	    Parking
	    Water butts	

	Stage 2 – Design protocol
	    Internals
	    Extras	

	Stage 3 – Design protocol – materials	

	Stage 4 – Design protocol
	    Planning statement
	    Traffic/parking surveys
	    SAP calculations/energy use
	    Secured by Design
	    Energy rating certificates/design targets	

11. Planning Application	Pre Application Consultation	
	Submission/Progress timetable	
	Amendments	
	Approval	
	Appeal/progress	
	Conditions and Condition Discharge	
	Landscaping	

12. Building Control and Building Warranties	NHBC/Zurich/Building Control
	    Appointments
	    Inspection: progress and feedback	

	Building Control and Working Drawings Progress/Timetable	
	Issues raised from above special resolution	

PHASE 2: Design evolution *continued*

Item		Actions/notes
13. Special requirements	Compliance	
	Housing Corporation Scheme Development Standards (SDS)	
	Employer's design brief	
	Housing quality indicators (HQIs)	
	EcoHomes	
	Discharge Planning Conditions	
	Building Control	
	Key performance indicators (KPIs)	
	Any Special Needs tenants? (Adaptation to design? Cross refer: risk register?)	
14. Construction issues	Schedules of Condition pre-works	
	Site accommodation	
	Insurance/warranties	
	Drawing issue	Does contractor have all the most up-to-date drawings?
	Updated drawings	

PHASE 3: Execution stage

Item		Actions/notes
REVIEW ALL OF THE PHASE 1 AND 2 HEADINGS PLUS...		
Contract	Pre-possession Agreement?	
	Agreed maximum price (AMP) approval	
	Agreement drafted	
	Agreement signed	
Design information flow	Frame supplier (timber or steel/prefab frames)	Check coordination of planning and working drawing packages and site delivery programme
	Architect/designer	Resolution of detailed working items if previously deferred – e.g. design and build contracts
Cost review during process	What are the effects on agreed maximum price (AMP) if in Framework Agreement/ Partnering or Contract Sum?	
	Unforeseen costs	
	Register of Change Instructions and cost effect	
	Tracking of costs within minutes: variations/instructions issued	Add/omit to track valuation and post-contract
	Projected final account updated, say, fortnightly or	A rolling tracker report to be monthly

Chapter 2
Building contracts and tenders

The building or repair process can be unpredictable. All too often, the project's and client's requirements 'evolve' – particularly when the client has had a chance to review what their budget will buy when tender prices have been returned!

If you work through the processes described in this chapter (together with the project assessment checklist at the end of Chapter 1) you may find that you end up repeating some stages as the brief or budget changes. That might seem like a waste of time – but experience suggests that it is well worth getting the agreement correct at the outset. This may call for a bit of honesty from all parties; but bear in mind that your objective is to avoid heartache later on (when money runs out, the contingency fund has been blown, and the contractor has a pressing new job to move onto).

WHAT MAKES A GOOD CONTRACT?

There is no doubt that:

>   **a good contract should be in proportion to the size of the works.**

A thick specification, contract and tender document for a simple repair such as a re-roof is likely to have an effect on the contractor's tender price if they have had to wade through pages of (probably superfluous) material to get to the point.

However, that does not mean that the detail can be omitted. Even a simple letter-style contract should state what plans or specifications are part of the contract (pro forma contracts will normally prompt you to do this anyway).

So, whether it's a simple letter, or a pro forma industry-standard contract (e.g. one of the JCT suite, described later in this chapter), it should clearly state:

- the parties and their roles
- the intended start date and the contract term (the finish date)
- insurance provisions
- pre-possession licences
- methods of certifying progress and valuation/payment periods
- penalties for non-compliance
- liquidated damages
- defects liability periods/rectification period
- retentions
- CDM confirmation
- drawings and specifications (i.e. what the works comprise precisely)
- contractual method of dispute resolution
- the contract price
- changes to contract terms (in a standard form of contract pro forma).

1. The parties and their roles

This should be a simple matter of listing:

- the client
- the contractor (once selected)
- the client's agent and their role as either Contract Administrator, Clerk of Works or Project Manager, and so on.

Given my numerous experiences of mopping up other people's contractual disputes, it is worth clarifying just what the contract will require of the surveyor/client's agent.

As Contract Administrator (CA) the surveyor has a duty to do just what it says on the tin – administer the contract. This means that the surveyor has a duty to treat the contractor fairly (which may, very occasionally, mean acting contrary to the client's wishes), ensure that valuations of the works are prepared on time, and that they are sent to the client to authorise stage payments and so on.

The CA certainly has to be satisfied that works are progressing properly and to a suitable overall standard of workmanship, but should not act as a Clerk of Works.

The Clerk of Works superintends the job and acts as a quality controller or site agent by watching over the works on behalf of the client.

This is a distinction that needs to be emphasised to the client, and is frequently misunderstood. Sadly I have met one or two surveyors who also failed to realise this to their cost.

2. The intended start-on-site date and the contract term (the finish date)

Start dates and the contract term need to be fixed with certainty (but note that they may be listed in very different parts of the pro forma contract), because any requests for Extensions of Time from the contractor need to be established with certainty. The cost implications which follow from this cannot be identified without fixed start/finish points.

For anything but the smallest project, you should clearly state the Practical Completion (PC) date. In particular, the PC should be included on any contract for works where possession of the building is critical to the client (new works or a refurbishment, for example).

Avoid sloppy working

There is a frightening tendency in the UK to complete the contract document once the contractor is in possession of the site and works are underway, but this is sloppy, and probably accounts for a good proportion of contract claims which subsequently arise. On a small job there should be no reason for this to happen.

---

3. Insurance

As discussed in Chapter 1, and reiterated in the project assessment checklist, it is essential to make sure that all parties are clear about:

- who is insuring any existing buildings
- who is insuring the works before they are handed over
- who is organising any 'other' insurance to cover any special risks to the project.

4. Pre-possession licences

If the contractor needs to enter the site for preparatory works before the contract commences, the contract may need to mention pre-possession licences, which are, in effect, part of the contract and so may need to be calculated as part of the main contract price. These licences are usually drafted by the CA as part of – but ahead of – the main contract document.

5. Methods of certifying progress and valuation/ payment periods

If the bank is funding the work by way of a loan to the client, the contractor should be made aware of the process to avoid potential delays caused by extra administration. Sometimes this may involve a separate inspection by the bank's own appointed surveyor or valuer. It is much simpler if the bank will agree to accept the CA valuation certificate, which they sometimes will. (If the bank delays in forwarding funds for any stage, this will have a significant effect on the overall programme.)

Everyone involved on the project needs to be clear at the outset how and when they will get paid; and then stick to it.

Watch out for mistreatment of subbies

On larger jobs with sub-contractors, often the first and only indication you will get of the main contractor's first wobble before going into receivership is *lack of* adherence to the payment regime. Sadly some contractors treat all their sub-contractors that way all the time. Avoid them if you can. It usually shows in the long run.

---

6. Penalties for non-compliance

Penalty clauses are probably not really appropriate to smaller contracts.

However, you need to be aware of them, and so does your client, because they are often confused with liquidated damages (see below). Clients have a habit of insisting on the application of 'the penalty clause' when they actually mean the 'liquidated damages'.

LADs and penalties

Liquidated and ascertained damages (LADs) are the estimated cost to the client of not having possession of the building when planned.

A 'penalty' payment would have to be agreed as an additional and strictly punitive cost to the contractor for failing to complete on time.

In both cases, clauses tend to be reflected in a higher overall contract sum – and higher risk to the contractor.

---

7. *Liquidated and ascertained damages (LADs)*

You will need to explain the difference between LADs and penalties to most clients. If the project over-runs for a 'reasonable' reason ("what other sorts are there?" you may ask...) then even liquidated damages cannot be applied. Otherwise the client is entitled to LADs reflecting a reasonable loss (i.e. identified beforehand within the contract as a realistic pre-estimate of what that figure will be). It is not a penalty but should reimburse the client for loss of benefit where the building cannot be used due to delay.

And you would need to show that your pre-estimate of the LAD shown in the contract was reasonable – otherwise as a contractor I might well look to have it set aside by an adjudicator as a penalty being mis-applied, or simply an unrealistic estimate of the cost to the client.

8. *Defects liability/rectification periods*

The revised form of JCT contracts (2007) uses the (less-confrontational) term 'rectification period' where once we would have talked of 'defects liability period'.

This paragraph will simply state the length of the rectification period (e.g. two years after Practical Completion).

9. *Retentions*

Depending on the size of the job it is usual to have a 'retained sum' – a figure held back from the agreed contract sum until the Defects Liability Period has expired and the contractor has made good. A Certificate of Making Good Defects is then issued on formal contracts, prior to a Final Certificate releasing the balance of any retention monies. Typically 5% of the contract sum is retained until practical completion, reducing to 2.5% after Practical Completion.

If the job is very small a retention is unlikely to be appropriate, simply because the contractor is unlikely to agree to it. (The principle is good, but it doesn't always apply in practice – play it by ear!)

Some of the smaller standard contract forms do not require a formal PC certificate (e.g. the JCT 'Minor Works' Building Contract). But there is something reassuring to the client about a 'proper' piece of paper rather than a note on the practice letterhead.

By issuing a PC certificate you are confirming to the client and contractor that the works are reasonably capable of occupation or beneficial use, and that the contractor is due the contract sum less the appropriate percentage of the retention (or less any agreed snagging or finishing off works if these have been excluded under issue of a Partial Practical Completion certificate or where a project is completed in pre-agreed sections).

10. *CDM confirmation*

Many projects within the scope of this book will fall outside the main provisions of the Construction (Design and Management) Regulations 1994, as amended 2007. However, you need to know about them, and decide if the Regulations apply and if so whether a Health and Safety Plan (and 'F10' notification) will be needed (see Chapter 6).

Remember: even if the main thrust of the CDM Regulations does not apply, it is still appropriate to apply a robust health and safety process to any project – both as a matter of moral responsibility as well as for the sake of your own reputation.

11. *Drawings and specifications*

Unless the job is of the very simplest nature, there will be some form of specification, possibly also designs/working drawings and so on. These will need to form part of the contract.

It is important that the contract both refers to them and states that they are part of the contract.

The best plan is to attach a copy of any drawings or specifications (signed and dated by all parties) to the contract document. Then there can be no doubt (or less doubt if poorly drafted) just what works have been agreed within the contract price.

Any design changes later can be more easily identified, in which event the contractor will probably be entitled to additional sums for extra work, and any omitted items can be more readily established too, and then deducted from the valuation figure.

12. *Contractual methods of dispute resolution*

Dispute resolution is a ticklish subject and can be made as easy or complicated as you like.

If you do not include a mechanism for dispute resolution within the contract, then the 'Construction Act' – The Housing Grants, Construction and Regeneration Act 1996, Section 108 may apply.

However, the Construction Act does not apply if the contract is with a 'residential occupier... which principally relates to operations on a dwelling which one of the parties to the contract occupies, or intends to occupy, as his residence'. (These disputes will usually be dealt with in the Small Claims Court.)

By drafting a reference to dispute resolution in the contract you can decide issues such as who will be the appointing body for adjudication in the event of a dispute, and what route the dispute should take if the adjudication is not accepted by one or either of the parties.

If the Construction Act does apply, and you do not set out an alternative second stage process in the event that adjudication fails, then you might find yourself in Court, and the client liable for both parties' fees if the judge takes the view that you had been unreasonable and the 'other' side had protected their position with a Part 36 offer under the Civil Litigation Protocol.

(This used to be called a 'Calderbank' offer, after the case of the same name – where an offer considered reasonable by the party making the case is put forward. If the judge agrees, then the 'other side' are, by implication, not reasonable if they refuse it, and a liability for costs can accrue against them.)

Reference to arbitration as the contractual requirement for the second stage, and with each party bearing its own costs, might be more usual, but obviously you would need to consider this in the light of your client's requirements and their instructions before completing the contract.

13. The contract price

The contract sum – the price – covers not just the 'headline figure' but identifies any sums which are provisional or contingent and so on.

A bit of client education and explanation is well worth while, here. Clients – particularly on domestic projects – expect the job to cost what they agreed at the beginning. Perhaps this is not unreasonable, given our experience of buying even complex items such as cars for a fixed figure, and with a guarantee.

Unfortunately buildings aren't always so obliging – especially old ones that need repairs or alterations. Generally on the day you start on site you can expect someone with a large hammer to find something unexpected. And expensive.

Good pre-contract investigation work will minimise the risk, but it cannot be avoided. Generally the older the building the worse the risk.

Thinking 'outside the box'
You can insure against digging up an Anglo-Saxon settlement under the proposed new office/conservatory or the like... But many clients don't bother.

Then there are always little factors which can be missed on the site inspection, desk-top study, geo-tech soil survey and land survey. This year, I had an ammunition dump materialise from under an old garage block! It was only when one of the older local residents explained away the remains of the concrete floor slab and Nissen hut walls about one metre under the existing ground level that we knew what it was.

Luckily we didn't find any souvenirs that time, but about 20 years previously the builders working next to my office pulled out a ten-thousand-pounder (now in the local city museum) following an extended lunch break for everyone within a mile or so radius.

It happens; and clients need to understand this. They rarely budget for everything even when you have explained the risks beforehand. But at least cover yourself, and give them the option.

14. Changes to contract terms

If the project is simple or has been very carefully planned, the contract will be fulfilled to the letter, and to price. But sometimes things go wrong for nobody's fault; or the client changes their mind; or legislation changes mid-project. For whatever reason, the contract may need to be modified as work progresses.

Contract sums can be adjusted for a variety of reasons including any delays which are classified as 'reasonable' and which therefore warrant issue of an Extension of Time Certificate where the contractor has requested it. Examples include exceptionally bad weather perhaps (not seasonal frost or rain), or where the client cannot give the contractor full possession of the site because they have not been organised enough to vacate it yet (or frequently because they do not yet own it, or have not clarified the boundaries).

STANDARD CONTRACTS

Although a contract may be little more than a detailed letter, it is worth considering the range of standard contracts that are available to make life easy, and save time, stress and typing errors.

This section runs through some of the options that are available for the types of work discussed in this book.

The JCT suite of contracts

This is a group of contracts devised by the Joint Contracts Tribunal Ltd (JCT) – a body comprised of representatives of the building industry and professions. The JCT suite was substantially revised during 2005, and is now published and distributed by legal publishers Sweet & Maxwell (*www.jctcontracts.com*). The new contracts came into operation in May 2006 and, although they represent a significant change in style from the older versions, the basic content is essentially the same. (Note that further revisions were made in 2007.)

The main JCT contracts relevant to this book are:

- Home owner contracts (HOB and HOC)
- Minor Works Building Contract (MW)
- Intermediate Building Contract (IC)

Home owner contracts (HOB and HOC)

There are two simple contracts:

- *Building Contract for a Home Owner/Occupier who has not appointed a consultant to oversee the work (HOB) (ISBN: 978 0 418 82660 9)*
- *Building Contract and Consultancy Agreement for a Home Owner/Occupier who has appointed a consultant to oversee the work (HOC) (ISBN: 978 0 41882670 6)*

Both are designed for small domestic building work such as extensions and alterations, and where the proposed works are to be carried out for an agreed lump sum. Neither is suitable for use in Scotland. (A separate version is published and issued by the Scottish Building Contract Committee Limited (SBCC) for use in Scotland.)

The disadvantage here is that these contracts are unsophisticated and provide little control over the payment structure.

However, for homeowners who are determined to run the job themselves, they are useful and clearly written.

Minor Works Building Contract (MW)

There are three types of minor works contract:

- *Minor Works Building Contract, Revision 1 2007 (MW) (ISBN: 978 0 418 84860 9)*
- *Minor Works Building Contract with contractor's design, Revision 1 2007 (MWD) (ISBN: 978 0 418 84870 8)*
- *Minor Works Sub-Contract with sub-contractor's design (MWSUB/D) (ISBN: 978 0 418 82910 3)*

These contracts can be used by both private and local authority employers, and are appropriate for works where a Contract Administrator is to administer the conditions.

Formerly known as the 'Agreement for Minor Works' the MW contract is one of the most widely used JCT contracts and is suitable for many types of project. It might be used for schemes much larger than the contract was originally intended for when first published, but where the works were of a fairly repetitive and simple nature, despite being of significant value.

There is now a specific mechanism to deal with subcontractors. Given that the contract might typically be used for projects up to £200,000, the subbies involved are likely to be known to the main contractor and probably will relate to electrical, gas heating and possibly groundworkers.

The MW contract pro forma covers all of the essentials, and is set out in sufficient detail to cover most eventualities on small projects, so this should be a straightforward solution to many surveyors' contract needs, and most practices will keep a box of the contract pro forma in the office.

Take care, however: these pro formas are not cheap, and the documents are revised fairly frequently.

The MW contract does not formally require the use of certificates to establish valuations, instructions, Practical Completion and the like, and in theory a letter is sufficient for this. However, a properly set out certificate is well worth while and looks more professional. With a computer spreadsheet, valuations can be checked and adjusted each month or fortnight in the office and then rolled for sign off as required.

Experience suggests there are more valuation certification errors since spreadsheets became common than ever occurred when sheets and certificates were filled in by hand and checked by longhand mathematics. So don't get complacent. The computer is only quick if you check the results and keep the data up to date.

A new version of the MW agreement was introduced with the 2005 revision – the Minor Works Building Contract with contractor's design (MWD). (And a further version, introduced in 2007, covers sub-contractors' designs.)

Not to be confused with a 'proper' Design and Build (DB) contract, the MWD is similar in form to the main MW, but includes a contractor's design element. It provides a method for the builder to complete parts of the employer's (or in reality the architect's) design and Employer's Requirements (ERs) – perhaps the mechanical and electrical element, for example.

Intermediate Building Contract (IC)

The main IC is:

- *Intermediate Building Contract, Revision 1 2007 (IC) (ISBN: 978 0 418 84840 1)*

This contract provides more detailed provisions and more extensive control procedures than the MW, but is less detailed than the JCT's Standard Building Contract (SBC). (The SBC is beyond the scope of this book; suffice to say it allows you to build up a document specific to the job in hand.)

The IC offers a number of distinct advantages over the shorter and simpler MW form and is aimed at projects of greater value and complexity than the Minor Works. For example, it can be adapted to phased or sectional completion of the project – immensely useful, say, on a small development of houses, if you want to issue separate Practical Completion certificates. In reality these are Sectional Completion Certificates, and would trigger the relevant dates – on defects liability for example, as each house is completed within the scheme.

Further, the IC allows for the use of Collateral Warranties (which came to notice in the 1980s) and increasingly are a requirement of most developers/ employers. Contractual liabilities are effectively transferred to a prospective purchaser/Building Owner or tenant, and may be a critical item in the marketability of a project.

The IC also allows the appointment of named sub-contractors (using one of the specific sub-contractor forms, if appropriate).

Choosing the right contract form

In my opinion, the With Contractor's Design (WCD) version is not best suited to schemes involving any significant complexity. This version of the contract is necessarily longer and a little more complex than the MW version. The WCD contract suggests that it is appropriate for use where a quantity surveyor and a CA have been appointed. This is, however, consistent with the opportunity for increased controls over the build process offered by this form of agreement. Novation of specialist sub-contract design teams would perhaps be more appropriate.

Other JCT contracts

The JCT Jobbing Contract – once useful for small repair instructions and maintenance works – has been discontinued. It has, to some degree, been replaced by the Repairs and Maintenance Contract 2006 (revised, 2007), but note that the latter is not intended for use by an independent external Contract Administrator.

There is a JCT Major Projects contract – presumably not for the faint hearted; and certainly beyond the scope of this book.

But it is worth mentioning the *Design and Build Contract (DB)* (ISBN: 978 0 418 85100 5) and its various versions.

The 2007 Revision 1 is an updated version of the old DB, and if you have used the old form before you will need to look out for the changes – for example, the employer is now responsible for defining the site boundaries.

It is also important that the Employer's Requirements are very carefully drafted and checked, because any shortcomings are not the contractor's responsibility. (Be very particular about this – some clients rarely update their 'standard' document.)

Part of the attraction of this form of contract, however, is that it encourages early involvement from the contractor and the risk is heavily weighted against the contractor once the contract is in place.

Use of this type of contract needs to be considered very carefully: there are probably more claims on DB schemes than any other contract. This is probably because both clients/employers and contractors alike

fail to realise the limitations of the contract and indeed, in their haste to get on with the project, their own limitations or those of the site.

The format is suited to projects with only limited complexity and perhaps a degree of repetition or standardisation – an estate of similar houses or industrial sheds, for example.

Don't be swayed by 'good intentions'

Too often the contractor launches into a scheme full of good intentions only to find that the site does not lend itself to the Employer's Requirements (ERs), or an existing building cannot be economically adapted. The contractor then pays a financial penalty for delays in resolving the design or inability to deliver. And at the end of the day the employer has not achieved what it wanted either.

A complex 'one-off' design is not the place to discover the limits of the DB form of contract.

Better by far to try to resolve the design first, where there is any uncertainty. Fine if you are a constructor who builds semi-standard industrial units all over the country and only has to adapt a particular model to the ER.

Federation of Master Builders (FMB) Domestic Building Contracts

One of the main attractions of these forms is that they can be downloaded free from the FMB website (*www.fmb.org.uk*) although the FMB does request you to supply project details so that FMB members can contact you with a view to tendering for works as a condition of use). The Minor Works version is intended for contracts up to £250,000 in value and the Domestic Contract up to £500,000.

FMB Minor Works

The document is simple, but it is simple to the point where it does perhaps favour the contractor more than the employer when compared with the JCT forms. For example, the contract does not define Extensions of Time very tightly; 'weather conditions which delay or prevent' is given as an example. The contract does not suggest that this needs to be exceptionally bad (which is the normal rule) – so by implication there could be an obligation for an extension for any normal seasonal rain during the winter period.

The contract excludes liability for defects which pre-exist, or are caused by the employer, but there is no requirement for a schedule of condition pre-works, which would be a sensible prerequisite to draft into the agreement.

The first port of call for dispute resolution is conciliation – effectively mediation rather than adjudication. The latter is likely to be more rigorous in its approach and decision making, and enforceability.

The contract does not set out a mechanism for an external Contract Administrator, and while an employer's agent is not necessarily excluded, the contract has to be modified if one is to be included. This demands some care and consideration on the part of the person drawing up the paperwork. For these reasons the Domestic Contract might be more appropriate.

FMB Domestic Contract

This is broadly similar in scope to the Minor Works version, but a little more refined.

There is provision for a client's 'authorised representative', although the role is not defined in the agreement.

The contract includes provision for a Schedule of Rates to agree in advance the pricing of any changes to the contract. In my experience, this still relies heavily on the integrity of the builder; an adequately priced (and ideally itemised) specification being disclosed to both parties in advance is preferable – there is no requirement for this in the contract, however. There might be a temptation to add liberally to the hours on any variations once the client has been signed up, although in this case there is some additional protection offered by the FMB complaints procedure and threat of expulsion to any non-conforming members (assuming an FMB builder is employed, of course).

Since this book is directed at the surveying profession you may well decide there is more comfort in the traditional JCT suite, with a more defined body of interpreting guidance and case law behind it.

SPECIAL CONSIDERATIONS FOR REGISTERED SOCIAL LANDLORDS (RSLs)

If you are working for a registered social landlord (RSL) – whether as an external consultant or in-house – then some different considerations may very well come into play.

Sir John Egan's Report for the Construction Task Force in 1999 (*Rethinking Construction*, July 1998. *www.constructingexcellence.org.uk/resources/az/view.jsp?id=309*) looked into the way in which construction and maintenance contracts were procured and, in essence, concluded that the traditional methods of procurement were not satisfactory for the 21st Century and that things could be done better, and differently.

The EU Procurement Directive 2006 developed this view further, by coordinating procedures for the award of public works contracts, public supply contracts and public service contracts.

The essence of the Egan Report, as far as RSLs are concerned, is that by developing long-term collaborative working relationships with its partners in the construction team an RSL should be able to:

- ensure a long-term flow of work, which would:
  - establish groups of suppliers and constructors and their sub-contractors
  - work with consultants who will invest in a long-term relationship.

The theory is that suppliers, constructors, sub-contractors, consultants and the RSL will be locked into a process that *should* engender trust as projects are developed. In addition, this also means that having constructor input from an early stage will assist with evolving a competitive build or maintenance price. The concept works through a Framework Agreement setting out the roles and inputs of the various parties – similar to a contract, but different from it in spirit and some fundamentals.

Under this system, 'core groups' (equating to a construction team/project group) are set up for each scheme. The core group develops the design and acts as a discussion forum for the resolution of problems and the airing of any issues before they become a show-stopping significant obstruction to the process.

The overall objective is for the partners in the scheme to be transparent and operate an open-book policy – profit margins and costs are open to inspection within the partnering framework.

Budget or target prices are set periodically, and the team is intended to work in collaboration to meet or even beat the budget price. The budget figure is affirmed as an AMP – Agreed Maximum Price – for each project. A policy of 'pain and gain' can be applied to incentivise the team with a greater share of the profit where there is any saving from the AMP, or a reduced profit in the event of overspend.

All team members share in revenue or reduced profit – so collaborative working is essential for each party to maximise a return.

The most common form of Framework Agreement is probably the ACA Partnering Agreement, although many RSLs use an adapted form prepared by their own legal advisers.

The JCT has issued a new form of partnering agreement within the 2005 Suite of contracts – the JCT Framework Agreement 2007 (FA) (ISBN: 978 0 418 85160 9; at *www.jctcontracts.com*).

However, it is worth bearing in mind that many people think that the JCT version is not a true framework document; rather, it is a template for collaborative working (i.e. similar but not quite the same as the long-term commitment made within a real Framework Agreement).

The JCT's Framework Agreement is available in 'binding' and 'non-binding' versions. Essentially the non-binding is a statement of intent by the parties to it. Although this is a looser agreement, it may avoid any conflict between the normal JCT contract terms, which operate under the Framework.

Is partnering the most appropriate form of contract?

'Pure' partnering may not be the most appropriate method for RSLs or similar organisations such as local authorities. Use of carefully drawn up traditional contracts may be equally if not more effective by providing a clear boundary of relationships, timetable and a basis for competitive tendering. In this respect the JCT FA might well offer an advantage.

If approached in the right (honest and genuine) spirit this can be conducted in accordance with the NJCC form of single or two-stage selective tendering. With a list of regular tenderers this can be a profitable experience for all concerned, where working relationships and genuine collaboration can still be developed outside of the FA partnering system. Note that the *Official Journal of the EU* (OJEU) rules for publication of tenders will probably apply, whether or not a Framework is used.

There can be a temptation to let maintenance work on 'schedule of rates' terms, i.e. a previously agreed hourly rate for the labour force which is then totalled for (usually but not always) smaller repair and reactive maintenance jobs.

Personal experience suggests that, where time permits, it is usually much better to price against a Specification, otherwise there is a temptation for the work to expand and fill the time available – at considerable cost later.

The JCT DB may be particularly appropriate in this situation, where a social housing client is likely to be risk averse. For example, if the Employers Requirements are properly drafted and accurately define the brief then much of the risk (which should be minimal anyway) can be assigned to the contractor.

What you can't see *can* hurt you

Note to consultants and contractors: much of the risk element may lie in the ground – services, foundations, or contamination will probably represent high risk items in time, and design and build cost – so effective early investigation is vital if the contract is not to operate against you. This means early involvement is essential. Back to collaboration...

PREPARING CONTRACTS

This section discusses the preparation of smaller contracts such as the JCT Minor Works (MW), although many of the issues will be the same for larger projects.

The fundamental principle of preparing contracts is: proportionality.

Use the appropriate document for the scale of job. A carefully drafted letter is sufficient for very small items.

Contract specifics schedules

A contract specifics schedule (sometimes referred to as 'draft articles of agreement', for larger contracts) recites the responses, entries, and departures from the pro forma contract in the form of an accessible summary. This means it is a convenient way of issuing proposed contract terms (for example, within a tender).

If you are using one of the standard contract forms, it is well worth drafting a contract specifics schedule before going out to tender. This will enable you to quickly become familiar with any particular contract pro forma and any revisions which may have crept in since you last used that particular form.

A good habit to develop is to take out a blank of the contract you propose to use and check off the main entries in a simple schedule (i.e. list) format for inclusion with the tender document. Obviously you can only do this where you are confident that the contractors you are asking to tender will be familiar with the particular form. (Alternatively, if the contract is lengthier or unusual in some way, so that contractors are not familiar with it, keep a copy of the contract available in your office for contractors to inspect, along with any other background documents appropriate for tendering.)

The schedule should be included within the tender pack for the contractor so that all parties can see at a glance how the relevant 'standard' contract will operate and which clauses will apply. (The new JCT MW 2005 incorporates a schedule within it, and this is a good example to use as an aide-memoire if you are drafting a contract specifics schedule.)

Remember that where a block of flats is involved in the tender the client's position needs to be reserved, and the contractor needs to be made aware that the tender process may be subject to examination and consultation by leaseholders under the provisions of Section 20 of the Leasehold Reform Act (which has now been subsumed within Section 151 of the Commonhold and Leasehold Reform Act 2002).

Note that standard contract pro formas are copyright, so although it is tempting to photocopy them 'for information' or as a contract document, it is illegal.

The complementary aspects of putting together the project are dealt with in subsequent chapters; particularly, you should consider how the contract will dovetail with the specification, and where appropriate the CDM requirements, insurance, and services, and their timely diversion or provision.

An example of a contract specifics schedule for a JCT MWBC is given on the following page.

Where small works are the result of a HIP report, or a mortgage valuer's referral for a Building Surveyor's report or similar circumstances, a simple contract, schedule, and specification would be more appropriate. A suggested example – for a roof repair to brace sagging roof timbers under the increased load from concrete tiles, which have replaced the original slate roof – is set out overleaf. A 'contracts checklist' is provided on page 28.

A 'contract specifics schedule' (also known as 'draft articles of agreement' for larger contracts). This example is based on the JCT MWBC schedule

Header	Response
Form of Contract	*JCT Minor Works* 2005 Edition
Employer	Albert Aardvark Property Management Co as Agent for Owners
Contractor	To be advised subject to award of tender
Contract Documents	*JCT Minor Works Agreement* 2005
	Specification for Works
	Employer's Requirements / General Conditions and Preliminaries
Contract Sum	To be advised
Article 5 (*JCT Minor Works*)	Principal Contractor for the purposes of CDM will be as the main contractor above
Article 6 (*JCT Minor Works Agreement*)	Adjudication is to apply in the event of dispute
Date for Completion	To be advised by contractor
Liquidated Damages	At the rate of £200 per week or part thereof
Rectification Period	6 months, except where works are under separate guarantee
Percentage of Total Value of Works	95%
Percentage of Total Payable to Contractor	97.5%
Supply of Documentation	1 month
Contribution, Levy and Tax Changes	4.11 and Schedule 2 are to be deleted from the contract
Percentage for Fluctuations	To be deleted – Paragraph 13 of 4.11 and Schedule 2 to be deleted from contract
Contractor's Insurance	Minimum £3,000,000
Insurance of the Works	Contract clause 5.4B applies to the building. The Contractor is to insure site materials etc in accordance with 5.4A.
Percentage to cover Professional Fees	12% or a minimum fee of £1500 plus VAT plus Planning Supervisor fees in addition.
Adjudication	To be nominated by the President of the RICS for the time being
Base Date	01 June 2006

Contract, contract specifics schedule and specification

Tender letter

To: Robert the Builder

Dear Sirs

Re: 'Stackup', 1 Full Flood Lane, Little Marshy, Hants

We act on behalf of Mr L Tigious the owner of 'Stackup'

We have been asked to obtain a quotation for repair works shown on the attached schedule, subject to contract.

The property can be inspected by an appointment through this office.

If you are interested in quoting for this project please would you advise us of your price in writing by Friday 13th March 2008.

A schedule of the main contract terms is attached.

We look forward to hearing from you and thank you in anticipation of your kind attention.

Yours faithfully

D I Ligent
Chartered Building Surveyor

D I Ligent & Co

Contract Specifics Schedule

Re: 'Stackup', 1 Full Flood Lane, Little Marshy, Hants	
Client	Mr L Tigious
Agent and Contract Administrator	D I Ligent & Co
Contractor	To be appointed
Start date	Friday 13th April 2008
Insurance	Existing buildings to be insured by employer under existing domestic policy.
	The works and materials on site are to be insured by the contractor.
	Contractor to insure for all third party liability with minimum cover £3million.
Payment	Single lump sum payment on satisfactory completion of the works. Payment due within 14 days of completion, as above.
Health and safety	Clauses 7 & 14 only of the CDM Regulations only will apply. See pre-tender plan attached.
Specification	Attached
Dispute resolution	The 'Construction Act' does not apply to this project.
Contract sum	To be agreed

Contract specifics schedule *continued*

Health and safety

Site security	The property is occupied. Secure storage is available in the garage.
Sanitation	The house WC and washing facilities are available for use.
Special risks	The premises are occupied. The family have two small children.
	The existing ceilings are lathe and plaster with no protection from falling through apart from ceiling joists: provide adequate working platforms for safe access, working and movement of materials.
	There is no fixed ladder at the trap hatch – make a secure temporary access.
	There is no lighting or power in the roof. Ensure adequate and safe power supply and lighting.
	Working at heights externally: provide safe working access and ensure adequate side boards and mesh on scaffold or tower if used together with other protection from falling or dropped materials or tools as needed.

Specification for roof upgrades/support at: 'Stackup', 1 Full Flood Lane, Little Marshy, Hants

1 Install new grade SC4 softwood purlin to back addition roof at 1800 up roof slope measured from eaves. Min. 125 × 50 section.

2 Support purlin at each end – use proprietary joist hangers cut into gable wall, or steel angle fixed with resin anchors and stud bolt fixed in min. dia. M12 × 4 no. each fixing.

3 Support the inner purlin end under the valley by raising a new support wall from the existing internal/rear main wall in engineering brick. Allow for RC 100 wide concrete lintel to span any rafters as needed. Do not point load the lintel where it is open span beneath by placing the purlin on top.

4 Fit raking supports back to gable wall and secured on to rear main roof/wall wall plate fixed at 860 mm from each end of the purlin – or use one central purlin prop notched and screw fixed at the centre of the purlin and supported onto a 100 × 50 plate bolted on to the Party Wall. Prop min. 125 × 50 section.

5 Secure any rafter undersides which do not load onto the new purlin due to old bending using folding wedges.

6 Check and secure all rafter feet connections to joists in the back addition with screw fixings into the eaves connection. Use min. 75 galv. screws.

7 Use 38 × 5 perforated galv. MS strap to secure joists back to the Party Wall onto new SW 100 × 50 wall plate stud bolted into polyester resin at 500 c/c maximum centres.

8 Check support to the main roof rafters, allow for temporary fixings and support if needed before proceeding.

9 Slide alongside new purlin against bottom of existing in 125 × 50 section sc4 softwood.

10 Secure the new purlin. Use folding wedges to tension if necessary to the underside of rafters. Duplicate existing prop onto internal load bearing wall. Check and locate/assess head of wall for load bearing partitions (e.g. around the middle bedroom) and provide additional prop support where feasible or run props back to 100 × 50 plate on stud bolt fixings against Party Wall where rake angles will permit.

11 Check and secure rafter feet fixings to joist ends with screw fixings, likewise to wall plate in the main roof.

12 Externally: provide safe access. Strip out defective tile 'listing' flashings and renew in Code 4 milled sheet lead properly wedged secured and let into Party Wall mortar joints and lapped onto roof by min 100. Clip all joints in folded lead. Finish with patination oil. All works to Lead Sheet Manual specifications.

Contracts checklist

- Contracts save time and money, and stress, later on. Some form of contract, however simple, is essential.
- Contract size and complexity should be in proportion to the size of the job.
- Be clear about the price agreed at the outset, and what is included for the money.
- Establish well in advance what issues might delay the project.
- Early involvement pays dividends.
- Both parties should have a signed copy of the contract.
- Take account of 'special considerations' for RSLs and local authorities.

Chapter 3
Specifications

Writing specifications should be simple; and so should the specifications themselves. That is to say that specifications should:

- be written in simple language as far as possible
- be brief and to the point
- give clear instructions (possibly with a set of drawings to help) so that there is no doubt about what should be priced and what needs doing.

Unfortunately this is often not the way of things.

Mind your language
Normally sane individuals with a reasonable command of the Queen's English seemed to feel a sudden compulsion to 'go in for' legalese or embellish the specification to give it a suitable 'specificationy feel'. A document with 500 clauses all starting 'the contractor should allow for' is likely to be just a little tedious to the poor estimator on its third reading.

I urge all potential specification-writers to think before they write, to write more or less as if they were speaking an instruction to the contractor, and to adopt a logical progression to the specification – which might mean specifying by trade to help with pricing up on a large job, or room-by-room for smaller projects, or simply following the format of a Schedule of Dilapidations.

'SYSTEM' SPECIFICATIONS

Probably the most widely used system is that produced by the National Building Specification (NBS), a company that is part of RIBA Enterprises Ltd, and owned by the Royal Institute of British Architects (RIBA) (*www.thenbs.com*). Originally, the NBS published a technical handbook, index of suppliers and products, and a book of standardised specification clauses and guidance which could be incorporated into a specification using pads of pre-drafted outline clauses for projects, to be completed by the typist from a marked-up draft copy. Now, of course, this has been digitised, and a software version enables you to prepare and adapt drafts much more easily.

The specification formats are divided into three main categories, which effectively mirror the expected level of complexity and the JCT Contract forms (see Chapter 2).

The specification provisions are broken down by trade specialism to assist the estimator in pricing.

On the plus side, the NBS format offers some useful features:

- It creates a checklist for the specifier and helps ensure nothing is forgotten.
- It conveniently groups operations by trade function.
- It saves time because it provides a convenient form of words to cover preliminaries (CDM, health and safety issues, and so on).

On the minus side, however, there is a tendency for some users to become bored with reading and choosing from among the large number of clauses; instead it's tempting to 'throw in' everything in the specification from the software draft, whether or not it's appropriate. This not only defeats the object of the specification exercise but you end up with an overwhelmingly long and tedious document, out of all proportion with the size of job.

On small projects, it is far better to draft a simple, though perhaps less impressive, document which actually answers the needs of the brief (perhaps using the standard clauses for inspiration only).

Proportionality is king

While writing this chapter, I finished a small pre-litigation inspection of a roof and Party Wall repair. The cost of works should have been in the region of £2000.

My fee was some £1300 to sort out the bits the contractor had missed from the 3-inch-thick specification and contract document which the local authority had prepared using one of the proprietary specification-writing software programs. Everything had been included in it ... except careful forethought.

Frankly, I think the contractor had given up reading it on page 100 or so. Small wonder that some bits had been missed: a four- or five-page document would probably have been sufficient.

A GENERAL 'STANDARD' SPECIFICATION

In small offices, in particular, it can be helpful to draw up a standard list of preliminaries and specification/clauses or phrases for typical jobs encountered locally. This can then form the basis of many of the straightforward specifications that are likely to cross your desk. Roof strengthening is a typical example, where slate roofs have been tiled with no adequate re-framing carried out initially and some remedials are required.

The following sample specification incorporates standard 'General Conditions' which are suitable for smaller works.

Sample specification incorporating General Conditions

GENERAL CONDITIONS AND PRELIMINARIES

OF

The Workmanship and Materials Required
In the Execution of
Repair, Adaptation and Extension Works

Under the Control and
Reasonable Satisfaction of

A N Other Surveyors

GENERAL CONDITION AND PRELIMINARIES of the workmanship and materials required in the execution of repair, adaptation or extension works under the control and to the reasonable satisfaction of A N Other Survey Department

Order of Clauses:

1) Definitions
2) Contractor to visit site
3) Tenders
4) Plan
5) Water for the Works
6) Light and Power for the Works
7) Manufacturer's Recommendations
8) British Standards
9) Credit for Materials
10) Trespass
11) Rubbish
12) Nuisance
13) Noise Control
14) Gas Cylinders
15) Protection of existing & Adjoining Buildings
16) Protect and Remove
17) Watching and Lighting
18) Existing Services to be Maintained
19) Roads and Footpaths
20) Traffic Regulations
21) Handover and Cleaning
22) Welfare, Health and Safety
23) Day Work
24) Advertising

1) DEFINITIONS:

In these conditions and preliminaries, where the context so admits:

(a) The singular shall be deemed to include the plural and vice versa;

(b) The masculine shall be deemed to include the feminine;

(c) The following words and phrases shall have the meanings shown;

'**Supervising Officer**' means A N Other Survey Department or their successor for the time being;

'**Contractor**' means the successful tenderer, who will be required to enter into a contract with the employer in accordance with Clause 3 of these conditions;

'**Contract Period**' means the period from the date of commencement until the date for completion;

'**Works**' means any works of maintenance, repair, minor alteration or adaptation;

'**Employee**' means any person engaged, employed or otherwise used by the contractor to carry out works under this contract;

'**Authorised Officers**' means any person authorised by the Supervising Officer to issue orders, given instructions to, or otherwise deal with the Contractor under this contract.

2) CONTRACTOR TO VISIT SITE: Before tendering, the Contractor is to satisfy himself concerning local conditions and the full extent and character of the type of work to be carried out under this contract, and shall visit the site to familiarise himself with the type of property, the geography of the area, the supply of labour and the means of execution of the contract generally as no claim on the grounds of want of knowledge in such respects will be entertained by the Supervising Officer.

3) TENDERS:

(a) Once submitted, the tenders shall remain open for acceptance by the Employer for a period of 12 weeks from the date they are due to be returned.

(b) No alterations to the text of any of the tender documents are permitted.

(c) No payment will be made to any person or persons for any expenses incurred in arriving at or submitting a tender.

(d) The Employer does not undertake to accept the lowest or any tender.

(e) The successful contractor shall be required to enter into and execute a contract prepared by the Supervising Officer.

(f) The tendering procedure will be in accordance with the principles of the the Code of Procedure for the Selection of Main Contractors (CIB) 1997.

4) PLANT: The Contractor shall provide all requisite plant and equipment for the proper execution of all work which he is required to carry out under this contract, including scaffolding, tackle, machinery, tools or other appliances and everything necessary for the use of his Employees and shall be responsible for their transport to the place where they are required and for any necessary erection and subsequent removal.

Allow for adequate means of water disposal, to ensure that water from any source does not enter the excavations or collect on the site.

5) WATER FOR THE WORKS: The Contractor shall provide all water required for use in the works, by him or by his sub-contractors, together with any temporary plumbing, stand pipes, storage tanks and the like, and remove the same on completion and shall pay all fees and charges relating to this, and make good all work disturbed.

6) LIGHT & POWER FOR THE WORKS: The Contractor shall provide all artificial lighting and power for the works, including that required by sub-contractors, together with any temporary wiring, switchboards, distribution boards, poles, brackets etc and remove same on completion and pay all fees and charges relating to this, and make good all work disturbed.

7) MANUFACTURER'S RECOMMENDATIONS: The term 'Manufacturer's Recommendations' where used in an instruction means the Manufacturer's recommendations or instructions printed or in writing current at the date of tender or at the date of approval of an alternative sample.

8) BRITISH STANDARDS:

Where an appropriate British Standard Specification or British Standard Code of Practice (or BSEN designation) issued by the British Standards Institution is current at the date of the tender all goods and materials supplied and all workmanship in execution of the contract shall be in accordance with the standard unless a higher standard is specified in an instruction.

9) CREDIT FOR MATERIALS:

All old lead, copper or other second-hand materials or other articles or materials arising from the execution of the works are to become the property of the Contractor and due allowance for the value of these materials should be made in the Contractor's tender price.

10) TRESPASS & SECURITY:

The Contractor will be held responsible for keeping Employees strictly within the close vicinity of the works, and in no circumstances are the Employees to be allowed to trespass on adjoining or surrounding land or property. If the execution of the works requires that Employees must enter upon adjoining property, then the contractor will obtain the occupier's permission, failing which this will be obtained by the Supervising Officer on being notified in writing by the Contractor.

Keep the site secure and prevent trespass, including trespass by work people or plant on or over adjacent property. Ensure that the security of adjacent property is not lessened by Works activities.

11) RUBBISH:

The Contractor shall at all times keep the location free from all surplus materials, rubbish and debris arising from the execution of the works. The removal of any rubbish, debris etc. is to be effected by the Contractor without additional charge. Any rubbish etc. left by the Contractor for an unreasonable period of time, will, after due notification by the Supervising Officer, be removed and all costs incurred will be charged to and recovered from the Contractor.

12) NUISANCE & ANNOYANCE:

The Contractor shall ensure that in carrying out works under this contract, no nuisance or annoyance shall be caused to any occupier nearby, to any neighbour, or to any other person.

13) NOISE CONTROL:

Comply with BS 5228 'Noise Control'.

(a) The contractor must only use plant and equipment which incorporates the best practical means of reducing the amount of noise produced by the plant equipment which must be operated, where applicable, in accordance with the recommendations of BS 5228-2: 1997 *Noise vibration control on construction and open sites* and the Control of Noise at Work Regulations 2005, in relation to CDM duties.

(b) The maximum noise level from the site outside any building at the window of the occupied room closest to the source of the noise must not exceed 70dBA between the hours of 7:00am and 7:00pm.

15) PROTECTION OF EXISTING & ADJOINING BUILDINGS:

The Contractor shall not do anything, or suffer anything to be done, that is calculated to injure the stability of walls, fences or railings. The Contractor will be held responsible for all damage arising through carelessness or inadvertence in this respect. Every means is to be taken by the Contractor to avoid damage to gardens and trees, and the works carried out so as to cause the minimum of interference to the persons occupying or using the existing or adjacent or adjoining premises. The Contractor shall repair any such damage at his own expense.

16) PROTECT AND REMOVE:

(a) All furniture, fittings, stores, apparatus, carpets, vegetation and the like shall be carefully moved by the Contractor as necessary to enable the execution of the work to be carried out, at no cost to the Employer.

(b) The Contractor shall properly cover such furniture, fittings, apparatus, carpets and the like with spot cloths and protect them from dirt and splashes and, at completion of the works, replace and refit all such furniture, fittings, apparatus, carpets or the like in their original positions to the occupier's satisfaction

(c) Any claims for the damage to furniture are to be settled directly between the occupier and the Contractor. The Employer will entertain no claim from any party for damage or loss caused to the occupier's property.

17) WATCHING & LIGHTING:

The Contractor shall provide all necessary watching, protection, lighting and care of the whole works from weather, vandalism, burglary or other damage from any source whatsoever excluding only malicious damage, which is the responsibility of the occupier. All materials on the site shall be protected from damage or loss.

18) EXISTING SERVICES TO BE MAINTAINED:

Where premises are occupied during the execution of the works, any existing drainage system, gas, electric, heating and water services to the property and to any adjoining premises shall be fully maintained during the progress of the works, and the Contractor shall take all necessary steps to prevent any interruption thereof.

Any diversion or temporary disconnection of the services, which may be necessary in connection with the works, shall be done at such times as are convenient with the occupiers. The Contractor shall be responsible for maintaining close liaison with the Employer and the public utility authorities so as to avoid any disruption of existing services.

19) ROAD AND FOOTWAYS:

The Contractor shall keep all roads, streets and footpaths (whether public or private) free from any damage arising out of, or in the course of, or by reason of the execution of the works and shall keep roads, streets and footpaths adjacent to the site free from mud, dirt or rubbish arising as aforesaid at all times and observe the Bylaws or Regulations and all instructions issued by the Local Authority regarding roads or streets to be kept free from mud, dirt or rubbish.

20) TRAFFIC REGULATIONS:

All Regulations relating to the parking, loading and unloading of vehicles must be complied with, and all permits must be properly obtained in due time for works.

21) HANDOVER & CLEANING:	The Contractor shall handover the works, thoroughly clean, functional and secure ready for occupation and use as intended. Polish all glass, ceramic and other smooth surfaces. Test and commission all plumbing, drainage, mechanical and electrical services. Provide the Contract Administrator with all keys, spares and instruction manuals.

22) WELFARE, HEALTH & SAFETY:

(a) The Contractor, the Contractor's employees, sub-contractors and any other persons engaged in the carrying out of the contract works shall take all due precautions to protect the health and safety of all persons who may be involved in, or affected by, the carrying out of the contract.

(b) *Want Construction Work Done Safely?* HSE Books, ISBN 978 0 7176 6246 3 (*www.hse.gov.uk*).

(c) The Contractor will take every precaution whilst carrying out the works to ensure the safety of the general public, Supervising Officer's staff, occupiers and all other persons likely to be affected by his operations. The Contractor is required to take all reasonable precautions to ensure that all unauthorised persons and all children are kept out of the working area.

(d) The Contractor's attention is also drawn to the document entitled *Control of Substances Hazardous to Health in the Construction Industry* issued by the Construction Industry.

(e) All guarantees, manufacturer's guidance instructions etc. together with a schedule of the materials, colours, colour types and other components used in the works shall be presented to the Contractor Administrator or Employer for incorporation in a Health and Safety or Building Maintenance file for future use.

(f) Where the scope of the works is not deemed to fall within the provisions of the Construction (Design and Management) Regulations 1994, the Contractor will nevertheless have due regard to all health and safety provisions and conduct works in a way to minimise risk to the Contractor's employees, sub-contractors and any other persons engaged in the works.

(g) Where the works fall within the provisions of the Construction (Design and Management) Regulations 2007, the Contractor will have regard to provisions detailed in the pre-tender Health and Safety Plan and/or Method of Works statement, in producing the Contractor's Health and Safety document and to all other statutory provisions. The contractor's attention is drawn to the Construction (Design and Management) Regulations 2007 and to Health & Safety Executive Construction Sheets Nos 40, 41, 42, 43 & 44. Where there are any matters of doubt, these shall be referred to the Planning Supervisor.

23) DAY WORKS:	Where day works are contemplated, the Contractor shall give to the Supervising Officer reasonable notice of the commencement of any work (or supply of labour and/or materials) to be executed by day work. Appropriate time sheets shall be kept which will be certified by the Supervising Officer and returned to the Contractor before claims for payment are made.
24) ADVERTISING:	The Contractor's sign board will be subject to approval. No other advertising will be permitted.

25) SPECIFICATION

Specification for roof upgrades/support at: 'Stackup', 1 Full Flood Lane, Little Marshy, Hants

1   Install new grade SC4 softwood purlin to back addition roof at 1800 up roof slope measured from eaves. Min. 125 × 50 section.

2   Support purlin at each end – use proprietary joist hangers cut into gable wall, or steel angle fixed with resin anchors and stud bolt fixed in min. dia. M12 × 4 no. each fixing.

3   Support the inner purlin end under the valley by raising a new support wall from the existing internal/rear main wall in engineering brick. Allow for RC 100 wide concrete lintel to span any rafters as needed. Do not point load the lintel where it is open span beneath by placing the purlin on top.

4   Fit raking supports back to gable wall and secured on to rear main roof/wall wall plate fixed at 860 mm from each end of the purlin – or use one central purlin prop notched and screw fixed at the centre of the purlin and supported onto a 100 × 50 plate bolted on to the Party Wall. Prop min. 125 × 50 section.

5   Secure any rafter undersides which do not load onto the new purlin due to old bending using folding wedges.

6   Check and secure all rafter feet connections to joists in the back addition with screw fixings into the eaves connection. Use min. 75 galv. screws.

7   Use 38 × 5 perforated galv. MS strap to secure joists back to the Party Wall onto new SW 100 × 50 wall plate stud bolted into polyester resin at 500 c/c maximum centres.

8   Check support to the main roof rafters, allow for temporary fixings and support if needed before proceeding.

9   Slide alongside new purlin against bottom of existing in 125 × 50 section sc4 softwood.

10 Secure the new purlin. Use folding wedges to tension if necessary to the underside of rafters. Duplicate existing prop onto internal load bearing wall. Check and locate/assess head of wall for load bearing partitions (e.g. around the middle bedroom) and provide additional prop support where feasible or run props back to 100 × 50 plate on stud bolt fixings against Party Wall where rake angles will permit.

11 Check and secure rafter feet fixings to joist ends with screw fixings, likewise to wall plate in the main roof.

12 Externally: provide safe access. Strip out defective tile 'listing' flashings and renew in Code 4 milled sheet lead properly wedged secured and let into Party Wall mortar joints and lapped onto roof by min 100. Clip all joints in folded lead. Finish with patination oil. All works to Lead Sheet Manual specifications.

Chapter 4
Planning Permission

Whole books are written on the numerous Acts and Regulations that apply to the construction industry, so this chapter aims to do no more than flag a few of the key issues that you need to consider when taking on the supervision of minor works.

> **It is essential to always work within the law, and within the limits of your own knowledge. If in doubt about any aspect of the law or Regulations, always seek guidance from an authority.**

KEY POINTS TO NOTE:

◆ **Planning Permission is only a starting point. Many other controls impact on development – and may even prevent development, even if Planning Permission were to be granted.**

◆ **Some omissions can constitute a criminal act – such as unauthorised works to a Listed Building.**

◆ **Early planning and statutory services' investigations are vital to prevent projects from being delayed at some cost.**

◆ **Desktop studies and evaluation are *crucial*.**

Formal planning controls in the UK really started with the Town & Country Planning Act 1949 and have been evolving ever since.

Planning can prove quite complicated – even some of the guidance and advice issued by central government can prove self-contradictory in practice. For example, Planning Policy Statement 3 (PPS3) and the various discussion documents drafted during its preparation, coupled with the emphasis on modern methods of construction and system building promoted by the government and the Housing Corporation, seem to clash head-on with many local authorities' interpretations of how they want to see urban regeneration take place – with few mass-produced system buildings finding favour!

◆ **The primary source of information about planning in the UK is the government's 'Planning Portal' (*www.planningportal. gov.uk*), which is an on-line information resource for both the public and professionals (England).**

◆ **See also the websites for the devolved administrations *www.scotland.gov.uk, www.planningni.gov.uk* and *http:// new.wales.gov.uk/topics/planning/ ?lang=en*.**

It would be sensible to download (and to be familiar with) the following:

● The Town and Country Planning Act 1990 (*www.opsi.gov.uk*) (or similar Acts and guidance for the devolved administrations)

● PPS3 – Planning Policy Statement 3, which sets out the policy that central government wishes local authorities to adopt – and which impacts on residential redevelopment of brownfield sites and development densities (much of which may be topical for conversion projects/smaller re-development schemes)

● GDO/UCO Terms – the General Development Order/Use Classes Order (which is a Statutory Instrument, passed under the Town and Country Planning Act), which define categories of building use and where Planning Permission is required for a change of use or if changes are permitted between classes without need for formal consent.

> **At the time of writing, a Planning Bill 2007–08 is working its way through the parliamentary process, though we do not yet know when the Bill will be enacted.**

GENERAL PRINCIPLES

The essence of the current system is that there are two types of Planning Permission:

- **Outline Planning Permission**, which establishes a Planning Permission effectively 'in principle' and in accordance with the Local Plan, for example.
- **Full Planning Permission**, which is granted prior to development taking place.

Outline Planning Permission is particularly appropriate where a landowner wishes to establish the principle that development was feasible. This should add value to the land. A developer could then explore the detailed development options under the (more expensive to obtain) full permission route, taking account of the developer's house style, tailoring the scheme to their own ideas and so on, rather than being committed to a pre-existing Planning Permission.

An application can be made for full Planning Permission without any need to obtain outline permission first. Full Planning Permission allows the local authority to look in more detail at issues such as ridge heights, overlooking, materials, plot sizes and a host of other variables which might need considerable fine tuning before the site is approved for development.

Permitted development

Some works do not require full-blown Planning Permission and instead fall within the category known as 'permitted development' under the General Development Order (GDO), which permits certain classes of work and effectively considers them to have an automatic Grant of Planning Permission. Filling in a domestic garage and converting it to residential use, is one example that springs to mind.

In the past, some homeowners have assumed that small extensions and internal alterations did not require Planning Permission, but this may not have been the case. With the advent of the Home Information Pack (HIP), homeowners (and their agents) will need to ensure that the HIP includes a paper trail that identifies such works and any necessary permissions and inspections.

With this in mind, it is well worth confirming in writing what is and isn't considered permitted development with the local authority. As a professional adviser, you should also make sure that your clients are aware of their obligations.

See government circular: Guidance on Changes to the Development Control System, ODPM 08/2005 (*www.communities.gov.uk/publications/planningandbuilding/circularguidance*).

PRELIMINARY ENQUIRIES

Whether you are an applicant and their agent, or the Planning Officer assessing an application, your first point of reference will be the Local Plan. This interprets the County Council's Strategic Development Plan at a local level. Both the Strategic Development Plan, and the Local Plan are reviewed every few years; with additional monitoring by central government to ensure that these Plans fall into line with national-level policies as well as local community needs.

Among other things the Local Plan will establish the Settlement Boundary – a line around the developed area of a town, city or village. There would be a tendency to presume any new development should only take place within this boundary unless an exception case can be proven. For example, a Registered Social Landlord (RSL) could demonstrate a rural housing need, thus releasing a site that would not otherwise be developed.

Having checked the Local Plan, your second point of reference is the relevant Local Planning Officer, who will look at the development viability in more detail.

By and large, Planning Officers are quite amenable to 'pre-application consultations', although they are under as much pressure of time and deadlines as the rest of us, to such an extent that some local authorities charge for such consultation meetings (although householders are often exempt from payment).

If you are acting for an RSL you may find it helpful to arrange a consultation with the planners via the Local Housing Needs Officer, and get them to run the meeting with a view to determining if the proposal will meet the target occupiers as assessed by the Local Authority Housing Needs Department.

Key considerations

Density

If you are dealing with a simple residential extension this is likely to be a comparatively simple matter. But density will definitely be an issue if you are looking at a redevelopment opportunity (from building a single new house in an existing garden plot to a much larger scheme). The Local Plan will certainly have something to say about this, but so may PPS 3 and the local authority should have a stated view on how they are interpreted.

Issues such as sustainable development and affordable housing will also come into play here. Section 106 of the Town and Country Planning Act allows the local authority to require a developer to contribute a proportion of the new housing as affordable social housing units, so it is essential to check on local requirements, as this can affect the viability of the project.

Change of use

Conversion of shops to flats is perhaps one of the most commonly encountered issues, and Planning Officers may be very resistant to creating a 'missing tooth' effect caused by the blank frontages in an otherwise established retail position.

On the other hand, in a fairly commercial location there may be impetus for redevelopment and reuse of existing (though redundant) buildings, so negotiation with the planners is always worthwhile. Evidence such as a report from a local commercial estate agent proving lack of commercial viability or perhaps the previous marketing history (unsuccessful) for a site may also help release sites for development.

Conservation Area

Unauthorised works to a Listed Building constitute a criminal offence, so early consultation with the Listed Buildings Officer is required. If you are unsure, do not take the client's word for it that the structure is not a Listed one – check by telephone and follow it up in writing.

There are circumstances where the work might not constitute an offence where proceedings would be enforced (essentially where works are carried out in an emergency to preserve the building) – but it is rare for this to be an acceptable excuse unless the structure is at risk of imminent and unforeseen collapse!

Conservation Area status can also impact on the style or implementation of works, and while it is less proscriptive than a formal Listing, it will influence the way in which refurbishment or new works are carried out to make them sympathetic to the tone of the designated conservation area boundaries.

HOW THE SYSTEM WORKS

Planning Application forms can usually be downloaded from the local authority's website, or hard copies requested by post, together with a schedule to help you calculate the local authority's fees (usually based on the predicted cost of the project or the number of new dwellings).

You should:

● Send four copies of the forms, and of all relevant plans and specifications required by the local authority. Include a declaration affirming ownership of the land or that the owner has otherwise been informed of the impending Planning Application.
● Ensure a receipt is obtained as soon as the application is deposited. (Some local authorities have been criticised by the National Audit Office for only registering the application when it has been examined – up to several weeks after it has been deposited.)

The Planning Committee

Smaller schemes (typically alterations and extensions) are generally dealt with as a 'delegated matter'; that is, the Planning Officer is given the discretion to make a decision on behalf of the council. If the scheme is a small one the usual process period for determination of the application is eight weeks.

If objections are received when the application is notified, the committee (elected members) must then consider it.

Larger schemes are generally given more extensive consultation, e.g. with the Highways Department or with service providers, and normally run to a 13-week decision process.

If any objections are received or the proposal is a larger one it will go before the Planning Committee for review. The committee, made up of local ward councillors, usually sits monthly.

The Planning Officer will have advised the committee on the merits of the scheme in accordance with the local Planning Policy. The committee then makes a decision whether to approve or reject the application, and if approved whether and what conditions or restrictions should apply.

Minor changes to plans

Sometimes it is necessary to make relatively small changes after a Planning Application has been approved. Common reasons for changes include poor boundary and title checks, or inadequate enquiries about existing services culminating in a mains sewer or gas pipe being located beneath the proposed development.

Any such changes must be minor in character and not affect the essence of the scheme. In this instance a written application for a minor amendment can be made. There is sometimes a (comparatively) small fee required.

Appeals

Rejections are not uncommon, especially where objections have been received. If there are elements of the proposal that are contentious, then the Planning Department may enter into a dialogue with the applicant or their agent, and this can provide the opportunity to withdraw, or amend and resubmit a scheme at no extra fee cost.

The appeal process could easily take another six months and an amended application to the local authority run in tandem might be cheaper if the development programme is pressing.

Attend the planning meeting
Sometimes the councillors can reject for reasons which may be more political than related to planning policy (although, at least in theory, this should not occur). For this reason it is well worth attending the committee meeting. If it becomes apparent that the rejection is not on planning grounds (or at least only ostensibly so) then you may have very good grounds for appeal (which is a free application, apart from any adviser's costs, of course).

PLANNING CONDITIONS

Very often the Grant of Planning Permission is accompanied by a range of Planning Conditions. These might relate to landscaping issues, approval of building materials prior to construction, or any other related matters which perhaps have not been specified in the application, or where control measures are deemed particularly important by the local authority.

Recent case law emphasises that where the Planning Permission states these must be resolved before development takes place... then they *must*. Failure to do so could void the Planning Permission entirely, and local authority enforcement action would be successful. Implications for delay and cost might be considerable.

It is common for developers to press on regardless and resolve the conditions as works progress. However, case law makes it quite clear that this approach risks far more than just progress on site – it is the viability of the whole scheme and any value attributed to it.

If you are acting in any project management role or as agent you must ensure that the client and all interested parties are aware that the conditions need to be resolved first.

If the local authority is slow in responding to these issues (it is not unknown) then project progress can be significantly impeded – so the earliest resolution and chasing down is required.

Chapter 5
Building Control

Whole books are written on the numerous Acts and Regulations that apply to the construction industry, so this chapter aims to do no more than flag a few of the key issues that you need to consider when taking on the supervision of minor works.

It is essential to always work within the law, and within the limits of your own knowledge. If in doubt about any aspect of the law or Regulations, always seek guidance from an authority.

KEY POINTS TO NOTE:

◆ **The Building Regulations Approved Documents (ADs) form the basic framework upon which the local authority's Building Control team will judge any works.**

◆ **Technical compliance is becoming more complex, and you may need to seek expert assistance, for instance, to performance some calculations.**

◆ **Other statutory requirements may also apply – particularly those relating to services such as water, gas and highways.**

◆ **Full Plans may be a preferable route to the simple Building Notice, now that homeowners will need access to accurate records of works done when they sell their property.**

Just as planning legislation controls what can be built, where and what it looks like, so the Building Control

Service or Engineering Services Department of the local authority – also known as Building Control – have some say in the technical detail of how it will be built.

Building Control's primary source of reference is The Building Act 1984, under which sit the Building Regulations and related secondary legislation. The Building Regulations comprise:

● The Building Regulations 2000
● The Building (Approved Inspectors etc.) Regulations 2000.

Both have been amended several times since 2000, most recently on 7 April 2007.

THE BUILDING REGULATIONS

The technical requirements of the Building Regulations are broad and complex, so a set of subsidiary guidance documents have been created – and it is these Approved Documents that form the basic framework upon which the local authority's Building Control team will judge any works.

The Approved Documents and related information are available via the Planning Portal; *www.planningportal. gov.uk*.

The problem many professionals face is that the Approved Documents can be amended by the Secretary of State at short notice, and without the need to go back to Parliament for further authority – so keeping track of the latest requirements is no simple matter. Although changes are published via the Planning Portal website, you do need to remember to visit the right pages periodically.

The current versions of the Approved Documents are listed overleaf.

It is important to ensure that the contractor or builder is quite aware of the Building Regulations requirements and also to decide who is paying for the Building Regulations application.

Building Regulations: Approved Documents

Short title	Full title	Details	Current edition (Jan '08)
Part A	Approved Document A	Structure	2004
Part B (Fire safety)	Approved Document B Volume 1	Dwellinghouses	2006
	Approved Document B Volume 2	Buildings other than dwellinghouses	2006
Part C	Approved Document C	Site preparation and resistance to contaminates and moisture	2004
Part D	Approved Document D	Toxic substances	1992
Part E	Approved Document E	Resistance to the passage of sound	2003
Part F	Approved Document F	Ventilation	2006
Part G	Approved Document G	Hygiene	1992
Part H	Approved Document H	Drainage and waste disposal	2002
Part J	Approved Document J	Combustion appliances and fuel storage systems	2002
Part K	Approved Document K	Protection from falling collision and impact	1998
Part L: Dwellings	Approved Document L1A	Conservation of fuel and power (New dwellings)	2006
	Approved Document L1B	Conservation of fuel and power (Existing dwellings)	2006
Part L: Buildings other than dwellings	Approved Document L2A	Conservation of fuel and power (New buildings other than dwellings)	2006
	Approved Document L2B	Conservation of fuel and power (Existing buildings other than dwellings)	2006
Part M	Approved Document M	Access to and use of buildings	2004
Part N	Approved Document N	Glazing	1998
Part P	Approved Document P	Electrical safety – Dwellings	2006

Some contractors are quite capable of resolving all of the Building Regulations issues – but both parties need to be clear in advance who will be paying for the fees and if these are to be included in the contract sum.

Some of the smaller contractors – often, but not always, the one- or two-person variety – seem to consider that Building Regulations are an optional extra. It is essential that it is made quite clear at the outset that the Regulations will apply.

The case of the arachnoid builder
A few years ago I was called in to look at a very leaky new chimney on a four-storey townhouse.

There was scaffold only at the front of the building. "It's cheaper that way," the contractor informed me, adding that he had never fallen off a roof in thirty years. (I presume he was related to Spiderman.)

He continued: "...And if [the client] wanted the **** chimney built to **** Building Regulations, well that would've cost extra!"

So the tray and flashings (among other items) had been omitted. I never really managed to find out why, because I didn't have the courage to continue the argument while clinging to the meagre front elevation scaffolding some 40 or more feet up in the air...

Routes to compliance

Previous versions of the Approved Documents contained 'deemed to satisfy' tables for items such as joist sizes, roof frame timbers and so on, but in their current form the Approved Documents are no longer 'complete'. Instead, the Approved Documents set out the objectives that the structure should achieve. All is not lost, however, as other organisations publish 'Deemed to Satisfy' guidance that can be very helpful – for example, the Timber Research and Development Association (TRADA) publishes *Span tables for solid timber members in floors, ceilings and roofs for dwellings*, a handbook setting out strategies that will be acceptable for most common timber building components.

British and European Standards (BSEN)

It is worth noting that the Building Regulations are not the only way of complying with the Building Act. The Regulations also list British Standard European Normative (BSEN) numbers which correlate to each appropriate part of the Approved Documents, and these often provide another route to compliance.

The BSEN are sometimes much more rigorous in what they demand. However, the level of detail contained in them, despite the inherent complexities, may enable a solution to be tailored to a particular project.

Rules of thumb won't do
Increasingly, there is a need to prove technical compliance with the various elements of the Building Regulations, and the more traditional rules of thumb that some of us have relied on simply will not do.

For instance, the old British Standard 446 has recently been phased out. In fact, this BS had not been cited in Approved Document A for many years, although it still applied until its recent withdrawal. This is a pity, because this was a comparatively simple British Standard that you could use for beam or stanchion calculations, especially if you had the appropriate computer software.

Likewise the new Approved Document L requires pressure testing of new buildings, and a theoretical calculation will no longer suffice.

Robust Standard Details

If you are operating in a smaller practice which does not have access to engineers or Building Surveyors who are familiar with structural, thermal, or acoustic performance calculations, then you need to look at other strategies for producing simple designs which will satisfy the Building Regulations (and the requirements of your professional indemnity (PI) insurance), and yet still remain cost-effective on the smaller and simpler projects.

'Robust Standard Details' (*www.robustdetails.com*) are one answer and provide standardised solutions to typical problems.

The Details handbook costs some £60 or so at the time of writing but it is a worthwhile investment if you find yourself getting drawn into more and more design work (or indeed as a Building Surveyor it provides a useful point of reference for modern Best Practice when considering defects analysis on new properties).

Additionally, many of the manufacturers or suppliers are able to offer solutions or calculations for their products if sent the relevant plans, drawings, sections or photographs. Steel lintels are a common example – these can be checked to prove the loads, provided all of the wall areas can be measured (and floor areas and joist positions if appropriate and bearing into the load triangle of the wall).

Drain manufacturers will also generally oblige with discharge/surcharge calculations. Certainly it is well worth making the enquiry if you are not confident with the calculations but do not want to justify the expense of an engineer or suitably qualified Building Surveyor to do the maths for you.

OTHER STATUTORY REQUIREMENTS

In addition to meeting Building Regulations requirements you may need to consider the various statutory requirements for services.

If you are only dealing with maintenance work this is unlikely to be a problem, but as soon as you start extending, altering, or doing significant refurbishment on new building works you need to give serious consideration to the following:

- Will the existing services network cope if any new demand is placed on it?
- Will there be any significant extra costs for service connections?
- Will any services need diversion works (often a problem for new build on a brownfield site)?
- Will any legal agreements be needed for easements or wayleaves for new connections?
- Will any licences be needed to excavate on work alongside an adopted main road?

All these are questions that Building Control will be asking, so advanced preparation is essential. There is a bewildering array of various legal 'Section Agreements' which may be required by the local authority or the service provider. The checklist on the next page picks out the key questions that may be asked.

BUILDING NOTICE OR FULL APPLICATION?

Two routes are open to obtain Building Control approval on a project:

- Building Notice – This is directed at smaller, simpler projects (not commercial ones – domestic only) where no considerable calculation is involved (for example, installing a new window and lintel, or reinforcing a roof frame to accommodate the load from concrete tiles). This is a quick, simple and sometimes cheaper route than the full application.
- Full Plans – This is more appropriate for complex works. The Full Plans route may become increasingly important to property owners if this is the only route to obtaining records of Building Control plans approval.

There is no precise line drawn between the choice of Full Plans and Building Notice. Whichever route is the most appropriate, common sense should prevail, assisted by advice from the Building Control Department staff, if you are unsure.

If you opt for the Building Notice, remember to ensure that a Compliance Certificate is obtained on satisfactory completion of the works. Although the local authority may record that the Building Control Officer has completed the inspection, a certificate is not always issued unless a separate and additional payment is made. Not all local authorities issue certificates; indeed they are not obliged to, although the authority should record the approval.

Given the culture that is likely to evolve under the HIPs regime, it seems sensible to obtain a certificate as soon as possible so that it can be packaged with all of the other property sales documentation when required.

If you are dealing with commercial property, then the certificate and related documentation should all be incorporated within the Building Maintenance Manual and Health & Safety File. In any case, the due diligence process on a sale of commercial property typically requires a business transfer under the revised Law Society Model Enquiry Form, and it is only sensible to document building operations and any approvals wherever possible.

WORKING WITH BUILDING CONTROL

A fee is paid to the local authority's Building Control department based on the anticipated cost of works. The Building Control Officers (BCOs) are then tasked with checking that the project meets a minimum set of criteria for an increasingly broad set of Building Control issues.

Before submitting your application, it is well worth discussing any concerns with a BCO. By their very nature BCOs tend to be practical people, some with a huge range of experience. They may also have some latitude and discretion to accept a proposed solution – albeit with some modifications to suit the situation in hand.

Make friends with the BCOs

In my opinion BCOs are among the most helpful professionals you can find within local government and are well worth consulting. But don't expect them to do your job for you. As a professional you are required to deliver the appropriate solution if you are taking a fee for it!

Bear in mind, however, that there is more than one way to skin a cat: the Building Act provides for an 'approved inspector' scheme, and it is possible to use external inspectors (under the aegis of the NHBC for example). Although perhaps aimed at large-scale New Build developments, the option is nevertheless there.

Services 'section agreements' checklist

Service	Considerations	Notes
Water	Mains potable supply?	
	Foul water drainage?	
	Surface water drainage?	You will need contingency plans if SUDS (sustainable urban drainage systems) such as soakaways are not feasible.
Electricity	High or low voltage supply?	
	System capacity?	
	Above or below ground?	
Gas	Where are the pipes?	
	What is the capacity?	
Telecoms	Where and what is available?	
Roads/ highways	Adoption Agreements?	At the moment, the main developments can be dealt with by a Section 38 Highways Act (HA) Agreement unless the Local Highways Authority is minded otherwise.
		This will allow the contractor to carry out the works with the design and site works approved and inspected by the local authority for adoption on completion.
		Works can normally take place while the adoption is being negotiated, and final adoption can take place on payment of the inspection fee and works warranty to the Local Highway Authority. But check first.
	Crossovers and new road entrances?	Section 184 Highway Act works include: the building of entrances to garages, private parking bays, or the creation of a highway entrance to 'Section 38 roads' within the site boundary.
	Major works to existing public highway required for developments purposes?	These would be Section 278 Highway Act works.
		These works must be agreed in principle with the Local Highway Authority, be technically audited and safety audited and the necessary legal agreement signed with 'bound' drawings before works can take place on the existing highway.
		The legal agreement can take months to complete. Ask the local authority if a temporary works agreement can be reached subject to clients' written undertaking to complete the Section 278 works. Find out the cost before your client agrees, though.
	Need to temporarily open up the existing highway and later reinstate as existing?	Covered by Section 171 of The Highways Act.
	Need to return land beneath the road to the original owners or those plots to which the frontage would return?	You will need Section 247 – Stopping-up Order under the Highways Act.
		This process to stop up existing highway can take time, as various Notices and plans need to be lodged and advertised for public consultation prior to any closure or working on the existing public highway.
		Do not underestimate the potential for delays, and investigate well in advance with the Highways Authority where appropriate.

Chapter 6
CDM and health and safety

This chapter summarises the key changes to the Construction Design and Management (CDM) Regulations that were introduced in 2007.

> **It is essential to always work within the law, and within the limits of your own knowledge. If in doubt about any aspect of the law or Regulations, always seek guidance from an authority.**

KEY POINTS TO NOTE:

◆ **The CDM Regulations 2007 have now completely replaced the 1995 system.**

◆ **The CDM Regulations aim to ensure that designers evolve a design that considers both safety of construction and subsequent maintenance of the building.**

◆ **Regular inspection of the site is required.**

◆ **Site records need to be as meticulous as possible.**

◆ **The Planning Supervisor is now known as a Coordinator.**

◆ **Additional training is highly recommended.**

◆ **The client's duties have been reinforced; the building's owner/occupier needs to appreciate their role in site safety.**

The original Health & Safety Regulations were introduced in the CDM (Construction Design & Management) Regulations of 1994 and the Construction (Health, Safety & Welfare) Regulations of 1996. These have now been modified into a single regulatory package.

A summary setting out the operation and changes of the CDM Regulations 2007 is provided at the end of this chapter.

SCOPE AND AIMS OF THE CDM REGULATIONS

The Regulations continue to have the following aims:

● To ensure that designers evolve a design that considers both safety of construction and subsequent maintenance of the building.

● To ensure, as far as possible, that designers cooperate with one another in formulating their designs.

● To provide a health and safety file which can be incorporated with the building management file (in commercial properties) to ensure there is a comprehensive range of information available about the original products used, any products subsequently incorporated, to assist with maintenance by sourcing new products which are compatible with the old ones, and to provide full information of any health and safety risks which might be attached to the use of any chemicals, finishes or building fabric.

Basic requirements

Regular inspection of the site is required. Site agents understandably become somewhat sensitive to any criticism, but a good one will understand the need for regular policing and, if necessary, that persistent offenders will need to be removed from the site for their own and everybody else's safety.

Site records need to be as meticulous as possible – not simply a collection of manufacturers' catalogues recording, somewhere, the specifications which have been used – with sufficient detail to identify exactly which products, paints and fabric have been used in the building and out of which particular catalogue.

When dealing with commercial properties (and to a lesser extent with residential ones) you need to hand over a comprehensive set of records to the client for subsequent reference. This may take the form of either a purchaser's or tenant's pack (something along the lines of the HIP pack, but possibly in greater detail), or in the Health and Safety and Building Maintenance files in the case of a commercial or larger residential property such as a block of flats.

It's more than 'common sense'

At first sight CDM appears to be common sense. Health and safety risks are obvious... Aren't they?

Unfortunately, experience on site suggests that common sense no longer applies once the construction team is in the thick of it; and simple and obvious precautions soon become ignored if there is no rigorous policing on site. I recently saw a classic example.

A contractor's mate was painting the skirting boards, working his way backwards towards the (open) lift shaft while chatting with the site manager, who was explaining that he thought health and safety Regulations were 'common sense' and he had everything under control.

When I pointed out the hazard, he quickly agreed that it might be wise to block-off the lift shaft before any explanations to the painter's bereaved wife became necessary.

It is all too easy to miss the obvious!

THE ROLE OF THE PLANNING SUPERVISOR/ COORDINATOR

Under the old system, a Planning Supervisor was appointed by the Building Owner/commissioning owner in order to assess the competency of the contractors and review the overall compliance of the project.

This has now changed:

- The Building Owner has increased duties of ownership for the health and safety of a project.
- The Planning Supervisor has become a Coordinator.

Projects falling into certain criteria need to be notified to the Health & Safety Executive under a form 'F10' (downloadable at *www.hse.gov.uk/ forms/notification/index.htm*) but there are exemptions: project notification will only be required if the project lasts more than 30 days or involves more that 500 person-days on site (previously there was also a category relating to five or more persons carrying out construction work, which is now no longer applicable). Nevertheless, clients, Project Managers and Planning Coordinators should be familiar with the Approved Code of Practice (ACoP), which explains how to comply with the Regulations (see *www.hse.gov.uk/ construction/cdm/acop.htm*).

If you are considering acting as the Planning Coordinator yourself, you will need to read through all the Regulations carefully and consider your competency to act, given the scale and scope of the project.

You will also need to:

- assess the risks inherent in the project (typically, scoring the risk on a numerical scale)
- assess how the contractor's pre-tender health and safety plan addresses areas of risk by either managing them or reducing the risk from any original proposals.

CDM is the one key area where surveyors would be well advised to obtain some form of training (for example, by a seminar or accreditation course) so that you have some form of documented competency that can be shown to the Health & Safety Executive or to clients who – as part of the appointing process – need to be assured that they have appointed a 'competent person'.

Remember:

As a specifier you will be regarded as a 'designer' as defined by the Approved Code of Practice.

You need to be able to demonstrate that you have considered the implications of the CDM Regulations, and that you have made adjustments to the working protocols, where appropriate, to achieve this.

On a larger project it may be appropriate to appoint an external CDM Coordinator.

Guidance documents

The Health & Safety Executive provides free information sheets and related publications at *www.hse.gov.uk/ construction/cdm.htm*.

A summary of the operation and changes of the CDM Regulations 2007

On 6 April 2007, the new and simplified Construction Design and Management Regulations 2007 came into force. This legislation revokes the existing CDM Regulations 1994 and the Construction [Health, Safety and Welfare] Regulations 1996; the latter now forms an integral part of the new Regulations.

The main objectives of the CDM Regulations 2007 are:

- to reduce residual health and safety risks on construction projects
- to improve project planning and management right from the concept stage
- to ensure the implementation of the Regulations adds value to construction projects.

Summary of key changes

1. Client duties under the CDM Regulations 2007 are more clearly defined, placing emphasis on their legal responsibilities.
2. CDM 2007 introduces the 'The Coordinator' [CDM Coordinator], who will replace the 'Planning Supervisor'.
3. The CDM Coordinator must now prepare the Health and Safety File and issue this to the Client on completion of projects.
4. All duty holders are obliged to cooperate with all project participants and all parties must coordinate their activities in order to ensure the health and safety of operatives and others affected by the works.
5. The role of the Client's Agent under the CDM Regulations 2007 will be defunct.
6. The Client is to ensure construction works do not commence until the Principal Contractor has made suitable arrangements to establish welfare facilities on site.
7. The Pre-Construction Stage Health and Safety Plan has been replaced by the Pre-Construction Information Pack. This will comprise relevant and project-specific health and safety information.
8. With the new Regulations, duty holders must accept a commission or engagement to perform any role under the CDM Regulations only if they deem themselves competent to carry out any such role. This additional requirement complements the previous obligation on Clients to engage only competent and adequately resourced duty holders.
9. The criteria for assessing and demonstrating the competence of Designers, Contractors and Coordinators is more clearly defined in the new Regulations and the associated Approved Code of Practice.
10. The criteria for project notification to the Health and Safety Executive (HSE) has changed. Project notification will only be required if the project duration is more than 30 days or will involve more than 500 person-days.

Summary of duties

Under CDM 2007, general and specific duties for duty holders are clearly defined:

- where construction projects are *not* notifiable to the HSE, general duties will apply
- when construction projects *are* notifiable to the HSE, specific additional duties will apply.

The descriptions of specific duties (below) are for projects that are notifiable.

Duties for the Client

- The Client is to confirm Consultants and Principal Contractor appointments under the CDM 2007. Where this is not expressly done, new roles of duty holders under CDM 2007 will be assumed by default.
- The client should appoint the CDM Coordinator as soon as possible and in any case before detailed design commences.
- The Client is to ensure construction works do not commence until the Principal Contractor has made suitable arrangements to establish welfare facilities on site.

There is continued emphasis on the Client's obligation to engage a 'competent' project team – the criteria for competence is detailed explicitly in the Approved Code of Practice. The Regulations clearly state that the Client should ensure sufficient time and resource is allowed for each stage of the project. This is to ensure health and safety issues are adequately addressed. Firm mobilisation periods for the construction works should be established by the Client in the development programme from the outset of the project. This is to ensure the Principal Contractor is allowed sufficient time to plan and prepare for the works prior to the construction phase commencing.

The Client is obliged to promptly provide members of the project team with relevant and site-specific information that is required to enable them to perform their duties and mitigate residual health and safety risk. The new Regulations place an obligation on the Client to ensure suitable arrangements for managing health and safety on projects are established, maintained and reviewed for the life of construction projects.

Duties for designers

'Designers' includes anyone who specifies or alters a design or persons who purchase materials where the choice has been left open.

- Designers are obliged to ensure they do not accept commissions for design work unless they are competent and adequately resourced to manage and mitigate health and safety risk associated with the project as appropriate.

- Designers are obliged to ensure the Client is aware of their duties under CDM 2007.
- Where a project is notifiable they must not commence detailed design work until the Client has appointed a CDM Coordinator.

The new Regulations require Designers to eliminate hazards on a project through design where reasonably practicable, and to ensure adequate control measures are established to mitigate residual risk on construction projects. This will involve considering all phases of project, design, construction through to maintenance, identifying hazards, evaluating risk, identifying risk owners and persons who may be affected by health and safety risk at each stage. Designers need to provide adequate information on significant hazards associated with design.

Designers are to ensure cooperation and coordination with other Designers and members of the project team, to facilitate the management and control of project health and safety risk.

Where the design is in relation to a workplace it is now explicit that it should comply with provisions in the Workplace [Health, Safety and Welfare] Regulations 1992.

Duties of the Coordinator

Under CDM 2007, the role of Planning Supervisor is replaced by the 'CDM Coordinator', who will, in effect, act as a project adviser on health and safety management. This enhanced and demanding role will require additional resource to implement the duties required.

- Advise and assist the Client with their duties, which will include appointing a competent project team and ensuring suitable arrangements are established for managing and monitoring health and safety on the project.
- Source and collate a 'Pre-Construction Information Pack' of relevant project information required by Designers and Contractors, particularly at the pre-construction stage, and advising the Client on any surveys or additional information required for mitigating residual health and safety risk on a project.
- Manage the flow of health and safety information between all project participants.

- Advise the Client on the suitability of the initial Construction Phase Health and Safety Plan and ensure that suitable welfare facilities are in place prior to works commencing.
- Prepare and issue to the Client a suitable Health and Safety File at the end of the construction phase of a project.
- Coordinate project planning and design work, advising on the suitability and compatibility of designs.

Duties of the Principal Contractor

During the construction phase of a project, the crucial task of planning, managing and coordinating construction work to ensure a project is safely executed remains with the Principal Contractor.

With the 2007 Regulations, the duties of the Principal Contractor remain almost unchanged. However, emphasis is placed on competence, the need for cooperation, coordination, the application of principles of prevention and the management of health and safety on construction sites.

Before accepting a commission, the Principal Contractor should ensure that they are competent to manage and mitigate health and safety issues associated with any such work; and that Clients are aware of their duties under CDM 2007.

Depending on the nature, size and complexity of a construction project, the Principal Contractor should ensure that sufficient resources are applied to the project to meet the needs of CDM 2007.

Prior to construction works commencing on site the Principal Contractor should ensure the following:

- a suitable Initial Construction Phase Health and Safety Plan
- welfare facilities (and ensure that the site is secured against unauthorised access)
- adequate and sufficient arrangements to monitor and maintain a high standard of health and safety on site.

The Principal Contractor should engage only Designers and Contractors deemed as 'competent', as detailed in the Approved Code of Practice. The Principal Contractor is to ensure that relevant health and safety information and associated training, and site induction, is provided as appropriate. Provide the CDM Coordinator promptly with relevant information required for the preparing the Health and Safety File.

Chapter 7
Neighbourly matters and the Party Wall etc. Act 1996

Whole books are written on the numerous Acts and Regulations that apply to the construction industry, so this chapter aims to do no more than flag a few of the key issues that you need to consider when taking on the supervision of minor works. I have also included one or two 'cautionary tales' that I hope will remain with you when you venture on site!

It is essential to always work within the law, and within the limits of your own knowledge. If in doubt about any aspect of the law or Regulations, always seek guidance from an authority.

KEY POINTS TO NOTE:

◆ **As soon as any work is likely to involve work to a Party Wall or a boundary, you would be wise to consider the implications of the Party Wall etc. Act 1996.**

◆ **A Surveyor appointed under the Act is responsible, in effect, to the Act rather than the appointing owner.**

◆ **Under common law there is no right of access to neighbouring land, and it is possible for an owner to absolutely refuse access to their property, or if access is granted, it can be on whatever terms the owner of the land wishes. However, the Act provides rights of access for the preparation of a Party Wall Award.**

◆ **The Adjoining Owner must be informed of any work to Party Walls or party structures (given Notice) at least two months before the work is intended to take place (one month for "3 or 6 metre" Notices).**

◆ **Party Wall work is certainly not an area to 'have a go'.**

THE PARTY WALL ETC. ACT – AN OVERVIEW

The Party Wall etc. Act is best described as 'enabling legislation', that is, it is designed to provide a framework in which the Building Owner can alter an existing property, or build a new one, on their land up to the line of the boundary wall or into/onto a Party Wall – a shared wall.

As soon as any work is likely to involve work to a Party Wall or a boundary, you would be wise to consider the implications of the Act.

Any actions that come under the remit of the Act will involve a **Building Owner** and an **Adjoining Owner**. Each may appoint a Surveyor to act on their behalf; and sometimes a **Third Surveyor**, who acts independently of the others.

As well as permitting the Building Owner to conduct work to a boundary or Party Wall, the Act provides some protections for the Adjoining Owner(s) and codifies good practice.

It is important to note that a Surveyor appointed under the Party Wall etc. Act 1996 is responsible, in effect, to the Act rather than the appointing owner – who ceases to become a 'client', at least as far as the Act is concerned.

Access to neighbouring land

One issue that is sure to arise when you are involved in minor works is the right to access neighbouring land.

Under common law there is **no right of access to neighbouring land**, and it is possible for an owner to absolutely refuse access to their property, or if access is granted, it can be on whatever terms the owner of the land wishes.

In other words we should all try to keep on good terms with our neighbours!

If the work is not covered by the remit of the Party Wall etc. Act, or if no easement exists, then there is very limited legal right of access.

However, the Access to Neighbouring Land Act 1992 provides a court procedure for gaining access in certain circumstances. This takes the form of an Access Order. Obtaining an Access Order through the courts can be time-consuming.

The application procedure is beyond the scope of this book; suffice to say, if things have reached the stage where a neighbour will not allow access for work to be done, you should seek expert guidance. Most Party Wall surveyors will be able to help.

Responsibilities under the Party Wall etc. Act

Timing and paperwork are fundamental to the correct operation of the Act. So, again, as soon as a Party Wall-related issue looms, check your responsibilities and make sure your client understands the importance of swift action.

The Adjoining Owner must be informed of any work to Party Walls or party structures (given Notice) at least two months before the work is intended to take place.

Notice does not have to be in any particular format, although the RICS and RIBA do provide pro formas for this. However, the Notice must include:

- the name and address of the Building Owner
- the nature and particulars of the proposed work
- the date on which the proposed work will begin.

Overall, it is the Building Owner who is responsible for serving the appropriate notices and for appointing a Party Wall Surveyor. Note, however, that the Surveyor can serve the notices on behalf of the Building Owner, acting as an agent.

Once the Notice has been served, the Adjoining Owner must respond (in writing) within 14 days.

The Adjoining Owner can agree to the works, in which case nothing further is needed than a written letter of agreement.

Alternatively, the Adjoining Owner may dissent, and negotiations and further discussions will then need to begin.

If the Adjoining Owner has not responded within 14 days of the notice being served, then the Adjoining Owner is assumed to have dissented.

If the Adjoining Owner wishes to dissent, they should appoint their own Party Wall Surveyor – usually (but not necessarily) at the expense of the Building Owner. However, if the AO is being unnecessarily obstructive, or if the AO was receiving some benefit from the works, then the fees might be divided up accordingly between the parties, perhaps under a Third Surveyor's Award.

The Building Owner's surveyor has the right to appoint a surveyor for the Adjoining Owner/s should they fail to respond, and also has a right of entry to inspect the Adjoining Owners' premises should this prove necessary.

The end result of the appointment is to produce a Party Wall Award, which usually comprises an agreement or statement setting out:

- confirmation that the wall is a Party Wall
- the scope of the proposed works
- any appropriate methodology for doing the works
- a Schedule of Condition to record the Adjoining Owner's premises prior to the works and to help establish the extent of any damages in the event of a claim under the Award.

Proceed with caution

Party Wall work is certainly not an area to 'have a go', and I have spent many hours as a Third Surveyor unravelling the mess caused by well-intentioned surveyors learning at their appointing owners' expense (or sadly in one or two cases, where bloody-minded surveyors have failed to work within the spirit of the Act and taking on a partisan role, effectively ignoring the requirements of the legislation).

SOURCES OF GUIDANCE

There are a number of excellent publications setting out the mechanics of the Party Wall etc Act 1996:

- Most Party Wall surveyors are members of the Pyramus and Thisbe Club (*www.partywalls. org.uk*), which is dedicated to the promotion of Party Wall education and understanding. This should be your first port of call if you are seeking a specialist. Another option is 'Find a Surveyor' at *www.rics.org.*

- The Pyramus and Thisbe Club's publication *The Party Wall Act Explained (The Green Book)* 2nd Edition, 2008 (*www.partywalls.org.uk/content. asp?pageID=78*) is perhaps the best interpretation of the current Act in a concise form. It should be on the bookshelf of anyone involved with Party Wall matters.
- The government has published a short guide too: *Party Wall etc Act 1996: explanatory booklet* – which is free to download from (*www.planningportal. gov.uk/england/professionals/en/400000000006. html*).
- The RICS Guidance Note *Party Wall Legislation and Procedure*, 5th Edition (ISBN: 978 1 84219 173 9) sets out some good examples to follow for any novice Party Wall surveyor, although if you are not interested in learning the processes involved it is probably safer to leave this to the hands of those with sufficient experience and knowledge.
- Also recommended:
  - Sarah Hannaford and Jessica Stephens (2004) *Party walls*, RICS 'Case in point' series (ISBN: 978 1 84219 152 1)
  - Paul Chernowyth (2003) *The Party Wall Casebook*, Blackwell Publishing (ISBN: 978 1 40510 022 9)
  - Alistair Redler (2006) *The Practical Neighbour Law Handbook*, RICS Books (ISBN: 978 1 84219 236 1).

COMMON PITFALLS

Here are a few pointers to help you avoid common errors:

- It is important that the correct notice is served – failure to do so might make the award invalid. The works might then result in a legal tort and fail to have the protection offered by the Act.
- The Act is a fairly short document when compared with much other legislation – and is reasonably concise. But do not make the mistake of reading the Act in isolation. There is a considerable body of case law which interprets the Act and which does need to be fully understood. The various brief guides to the Act are extremely useful, but are no substitute for a detailed working knowledge of the system.
- The content of the Notice is very important and it needs to describe the proposed works in detail – including foundation depth, for example. This means the Building Owner needs to have carried out sufficient research and documentation in advance.

The long and sorry saga of the semi-detached garage
I was once involved as Third Surveyor in a case concerning a pair of 1930s semi-detached houses. These were, in fact, the two unattached halves of two pairs of houses. Between them ran a drive, half owned by each of the houses but with a right to drive over the other's half, and there was a pair of garages within the back garden area which were semi-detached also – a very common set-up in the UK.

The owners of one house, in ignorance of the Act, sent an explanatory letter to the neighbour setting out their intention to demolish their half of the semi-detached garage and build a new garage further back within the site. Although the letter was detailed, it did not contain the correct information to constitute a Party Wall Notice.

The work proceeded, and on its completion the neighbour claimed for damage to his garage roof (asbestos cement roof sheets) and to parts of the wall, and claimed that the structure was now unbalanced and that the roof was sliding off, pushing out the side wall of the building.

The Building Owner tried to solve the problem by appointing a Party Wall surveyor to serve notice and supervise the repairs.

However, by now a tort had occurred. (They might have got away with it in the absence of any damage.) The Building Owner's Party Wall Surveyor proceeded to draw out a variety of convoluted arguments with the Adjoining Owner's Surveyor – over some two years – as to why the various schemes

of repair works he proposed were quite adequate given the obviously poor original state of the pair of garages.

He also contended that it was simply 'not fair' that his appointing owner should improve the neighbour's garage. Matters were not helped by the builder carrying out a variety of further substandard works to try and address the problem.

The Building Owner's surveyor had missed the point:

- His BO had acted in tort and had no protection from the Act.
- Damage had actually occurred.
- Certainly the garages were in poor condition beforehand – but how poor exactly? There was no Award and no Schedule of Condition to prove that some of the defects were longstanding.
- Certainly the AO was vexatious, tenacious, and determined to frustrate the neighbour, and was probably looking for a free new garage in the process (when some simple repairs were quite appropriate). But he had case law on his side…
- Relying on a copy of the 'Green Book' only – and ignorant of litigation developments such as the 'Roadrunner' case, which set a very good precedent – the BO's surveyor dragged the process out for some two or more years. All at a combined cost in fees of about three times the value of the whole job and about 15 times the value of doing the appropriate relatively small repair!

One major shortcoming (or at least an apparent shortcoming) is the cost. One, two or sometimes even three surveyors (or more if there are several Adjoining Owners affected) may be required to prepare a simple Award on a domestic project. (I have some sympathy with the poor Building Owner, who might spend more on the Party Wall process than the actual cost of doing the work.)

However, the cost of avoiding the process can be considerably greater if the statutory provisions are not followed, and the works can be injuncted (with delays and legal costs) or, if defects ensue, may result in a tort. Very expensive liabilities can accrue if any damage occurs. This may not be attributable directly to the works but it is hard to prove innocence in the absence of an Award and an accompanying Schedule of Condition.

WHAT TO DO WHEN THE ACT DOES NOT APPLY

There are occasions when the protocols set out in the Part Wall etc. Act will not apply, and the Building Owner will have no 'rights' (or obligations – for example, if proposed building works or repairs might include piling or demolition, or anything likely to cause vibration or associated damage), but the works fall outside the provisions of the Party Wall etc. Act.

In such cases, an explanatory letter to the relevant Adjoining Owner would be a courtesy. But it would also be sensible to draw up a simple Schedule of Condition that will be agreed by both the Building Owner and the Adjoining Owner. This would set out:

- the condition of the buildings prior to works
- that the Building Owner has (hopefully) endeavoured to take all reasonable precautions.

Something more detailed than a simple 'photographic schedule' is necessary. Brief text should suffice, with accompanying photographs.

This Schedule may be regarded as an insurance policy to properly establish the condition of the adjoining buildings before the works start and avoid at least one area for potential argument later on.

Chapter 8
When things go wrong...

Every job is unique and will have its own set of potential pitfalls and difficulties that you may need to circumnavigate. This chapter discusses the two key issues that you need to consider when taking on the supervision of minor works: failure to progress the work; and sub-standard workmanship.

It is essential to always work within the law, and within the limits of your own knowledge. If in doubt about any aspect of the law or Regulations, always seek guidance from an authority.

FAILURE TO PROGRESS THE WORK

A very common problem for Contract Administrators or Project Managers is that the contractor is failing to adhere to the programme set down.

The most common scenario is where a small builder effectively takes on too many jobs to be able to fulfil them all within the appropriate timescale, or is encountering cash flow problems.

In these cases it is usually straightforward to terminate the contract, if necessary paying for work satisfactorily completed to date.

Be aware, however, that if you commission a second contractor to continue with the works, the costs are likely to go up quite significantly because the second contractor will need to verify the work done to date and familiarise themselves with the project.

In the case of a contractor with cash flow problems, or one that has actually gone into liquidation, you will need to be extremely careful to confirm that

works carried out (and fixtures and fittings attached to the building) are within the ownership of the client.

It is not unheard of for sub-contractors to return to site to try and claim for goods to off-set where they have not been paid in full.

- Normally, once components are on site or constructed into the building fabric they come within the ownership of the client.
- If materials stored on site have been paid for by the client but not yet fixed to the building, it is sensible to obtain a 'vesting certificate' to establish ownership of the goods by the client and prevent any dispute which might arise later on.
- If materials are being stored on site but have not yet been paid for, this is another matter. The contractor might have a valid claim to take them back (or more likely, the Administrator would).

Contractual issues

If you are using one of the JCT contracts, it is likely to impose the requirement for the contractor to proceed 'regularly and diligently' with the contract works.

The case law is a little confusing in this area but certainly there is a duty on the contractor to be in attendance on site (i.e. regularly) and to proceed diligently – that is to say, applying suitable industry and application to meet the various timetables set out in contract.

Your ability to terminate the contract is likely to depend very greatly on the quality of record keeping – both by the Contact Administrator or Project Manager (or client) and by the contractor. Hence, the importance of maintaining written records and minutes of pre-start or site meetings.

If you have used the agenda format set out at the beginning of this book, you should not go too far wrong in recording the appropriate information.

However, many contractors are quite legitimately able to claim that they are unable to proceed diligently due to shortcomings by either the design team, Contract Administrator or the client. They may well cite:

- late delivery of information
- inadequate clarification of working drawings or Employers' Requirements
- inability of the contractor to take possession of the whole site, or boundaries which subsequently come into disputed ownership.

All these could be legitimate grounds for delay. These would also be reasonable grounds for the contractor to ask for an extension of time. This would mean that liquidated damages (or indeed any penalty clauses should they be in the contract) could not then reasonably be applied.

The ramifications of terminating a contract can be so severe that it would be appropriate to take legal advice (or rather, advise the client to do so) before confirming this course of action.

Keeping the records squeaky clean

Remember: the quality of your record keeping will be called into question and needs to be squeaky clean if you are to make an effective case for termination.

Failure to do so could mean that there is a case not only against the contractor but also against the surveyor if the client or contractor can successfully put a case that they were not able to proceed due to inadequate information or the like.

If you have not used one of the standard forms of JCT contracts then you will need particular regard to what form of words are used to enable the contract to be terminated for lack of progress or inadequate quality of workmanship.

DEFINING ACCEPTABLE STANDARDS OF WORKMANSHIP

A considerable number of professional indemnity (PI) claims arise due to inadequate workmanship on all sorts of new or repair works to buildings.

Sometimes clients misunderstand the nature of the work. For example, it may be appropriate to emphasise to the client that some of the cosmetic issues cannot be addressed – sagging roofs can be supported, but it is extremely difficult to take the sag out, even if the roof has been repaired to a satisfactory standard.

In other instances, a process of elimination may be necessary to try to remedy a 'defect'; so various repairs solutions may be tried on a suck-it-and-see basis. The question you need to address is whether the client understands this process. You need to ensure that the various options are explained to the client, and to keep clear minutes of site meetings so that you have a record of the options that have been tried.

For example, you may propose to carry out subsidence repairs by first of all repairing defective drains (assuming these were the source of the problem; which they commonly are). Once the drains are repaired, but there were no significant changes to the moisture profile of shrinkable clay soils surrounding the foundations, then the next step would be to look to other causes (such as trees nearby). Unfortunately, in this increasingly litigious age, a suitable and rather minimalist repair strategy for subsidence is frequently no longer acceptable. Most surveyors and engineers who specify repairs will require the building to be underpinned to ensure that there is no 'come back', although some insurance company loss adjusters may still be keen to adopt the former approach (bearing in mind of course that their client is the insurance company and not the builder owner!).

It is all a matter of expectation and you need to ensure that the client's expectations are appropriate at the outset.

Earlier in this book, I emphasised the importance of defining the instructions with the client, and this is worth repeating here:

> **If the client thinks you are supervising works (or indeed if you accidentally start supervising them even if not contracted to do so) and there are shortcomings later, you may end up with a liability for not pointing them out.**

As Contract Administrator you would have a much less onerous duty of care to the client than, say, if you were acting as the Clerk of Works, where attendance on site is considerably more rigorous and where a supervisory function is involved.

In short, if you are not in the role of supervising the works – don't. Any shortcomings then become those of the contractor, unless they are so obvious that they should have been picked up in a relatively casual inspection by the Contract Administrator.

Tact, diplomacy and record keeping

If you do notice unacceptable standards of workmanship you need to deal with this as soon as possible – tactfully and politely! Of course, it is essential to address your comments to the appropriate person. But proceed with caution because one person's passing comment is another's out-and-out criticism, and the situation could easily degenerate into a full-blown argument.

Above all, make sure that you have adequate records of the unacceptable practice. Photos of site progress are extremely useful in this regard. It is worth attaching them to site progress reports/minutes, and certainly leaving the photographs on file (for example, on a CD) so that they cannot be accidentally deleted from the computer before they are needed, should a problem occur (probably a couple of years hence!).

Should you need to revisit the situation later because it has not been adequately resolved, you will need all the ammunition you can lay your hands on, to:

- prove to the client that you have been diligent
- address any contractors' claims for delay, extensions of time, and so on.

PART 2 – Repairs: problems and solutions

Chapter 9
Walls

When it comes to walls, many surveyors (and a fair few builders too) grasp instantly for one of two options: condemn the defective building element out of hand; or endeavour to repair the element without due regard to the fact that it is beyond its economic lifespan. I have also noticed that a lot of defects endure an insensitive repair, which then causes further problems – creating a domino effect of defect/repair.

A little unfair? Well, I agree, it's not always easy to call the shots. So, it is always well worth stepping back for a moment and examining the 'apparently obvious' to test your initial response to any defect.

Therefore, before you begin to plan a repair:

- be sure what you are repairing and why
- carefully consider the age of the building and the materials used; in most cases it is appropriate to match the new material to the old
- don't skimp on investigations; it is usually better to make a large mess to start with than an even bigger one later.

In particular, if cracks are present, you need to establish whether the crack is historic or ongoing.

Although the smaller buildings that fall within the scope of this book tend to be of quite conventional design, you may well be faced with a surprisingly wide range of unusual circumstances arising from the day-to-day process of condition survey inspections and subsequent rectification.

The box Walls – the basics, should serve as a useful aide memoire when you are out on a site inspection.

WALLS – THE BASICS

9-inch English solid wall/Flemish wall bond
Both these types of solid wall construction are prone to poorly maintained pointing, or the wrong mortar being used; which means these walls can become wet (especially if in an exposed position). Joinery built into the wall can deteriorate over time. Watch out for cavity walls built to mimic traditional bonds – if in doubt, measure the wall thickness at door/window reveals to verify.

Half-brick walls
Nominally only 100 mm (4 inches) thick, these walls (often encountered at first floor only in Sussex and Surrey) have limited strength. Most mortgage lenders will not accept a two-storey half-brick dwelling. If repairing, consider a rebuild/upgrade to a cavity wall (or 215 mm/9 inch, if space is tight). Very limited weather resistance; often slate or tile-hung to improve this. Can be easy to upgrade with insulation and render.

13-inch wall

Effectively a 100-mm (4-inch) skin directly laid into a 215-mm (9-inch) wall, this construction will have similar performance characteristics to a 215-mm (9-inch) wall, but being thicker will have better resistance to moisture and temperature changes. The 100-mm (4-inch) 'skin' can separate, but this is usually easy to re-attach using helical ties, providing the problem is caught in the early stages.

Flint wall

Unlikely to have a damp-proof course (DPC) unless on a brick base, this construction can drain quite well because of the interstices in the wall behind the pointing. This type is very expensive to repair, however, and it is difficult to match repairs to the existing work. Pre-formed flint wall blocks/modules are available for new work or extensions. These need face pointing, and provide a fair match and good compromise for new work. Local defects in flint walls often lead to wholesale reconstruction of whole wall sections or walls, so proceed with caution!

Coursed rubble

Effectively a 'big stone' solid wall. Performance characteristics are broadly similar to 9-inch brick, depending in part on the quality of the stone. Weak bond laps can develop if the rubble is not skilfully laid, and this can lead to cracks and bulges (e.g. at door or window openings). Helical tie repairs are often effective, whereas that solution would not work in a flint wall.

Stone

A proper stone wall would probably have been expensive to build; and it is likely to be expensive to repair, and difficult to match the new work to the old. Some reconstituted stone 'equivalents' are available, but these have variable weathering qualities; after 20 years or so, some revert to the appearance of concrete blocks.

Cob

A traditional wall built of mud/dung/straw; often found in Listed Buildings. This material has to have an inherent minimum moisture content – if it dries out it will fail; too wet and it will collapse. Definitely do *not* insert a DPC or a French drain – both will usually have dire consequences! Consider appropriate training before getting involved in specifying repairs. There are numerous books on this construction technique.

Half timber

Traditional in England and Wales, the timber frames are filled with wattle and plaster or brick. Great care and thought should be given to any repair; the basics are simple but frequently ignored. Sympathetic materials must be used; and conservation groups may call for cosmetic solutions which a robust and equally valid traditional repair would not fulfil.

Modern timber-framed construction

'Timber frame' in various guises has been with us for many years, and there were periods of popularity in the 1920s and 1950s when various systems were developed.

The 'modern' timber frame really dates from about 1980. Usually clad in brick (the familiarity of brick is, I suppose, reassuring to the mass market), the timber frame behind the cladding bears the loads of the structure.

The frames essentially take two forms:

- **Closed panels** – the timber frame is enclosed by a sheet board material on both sides to create a sandwich. This offers good panel rigidity but it is difficult to incorporate built-in service pipe and cable drops; and it is not forgiving of any errors if they are wrongly positioned.

- **Open panels** – only one side of the timber frame is delivered enclosed with a racking board to stiffen it. It is much easier to install services and insulation before enclosing the internal face of the board with plasterboard lining or similar.

Done properly, timber frame offers advantages of speedy and accurate off-site manufacture. Done wrongly (not as hard as it might seem), delay and cost to the build programme can ensue.

Timber frame has been the darling of the Modern Methods of Construction (MMC) lobby because of the perceived advantages and use of a material with a low(ish) carbon footprint. The argument may change in the future, however, as concrete or brick mass products offer other energy advantages, which may perform better in the warmer, wetter climate predicted for the UK. The jury is currently still out.

Modern cavity wall construction

Usually comprises a facing brick with a concrete block-work inner skin, which often includes a lightweight block to improve the insulation.

Cavity widths have tended to increase with each revision of the Building Regulations to enable more cavity insulation material to be added.

Advantages:

- Easily modified or extended post-construction.

- Less prone to damage from water penetration (flooding, or poor detailing causing water ingress might have a greater effect on a timber-framed equivalent).

Types of brick wall bond

(a) Brick wall bonds shown in imperial brick coordinating measurements

Double Flemish in plan

8¾"

(b) Three and one variant of English bond (in elevation)

3 stretcher courses crossed by 4th course of headers

(c) English bond

Quoin header

Stretchers

Quoin closer 2¼" wide

Single Flemish 13½" wall

And with English bond backing

Materials

The majority of bricks found in older properties (from about 1800 to 1939) are likely to be of a traditional fired clay. If the 'London red brick' has been used, the brick is probably quite porous and relatively soft, with (by implication) a limited resistance to crushing.

'Special' buildings, such as old warehouses that might be subject to high floor loads (in addition to the loads and self-weight generated by being comparatively tall structures themselves), might very well use a more dense engineering brick. This is probably of similar colour to the London red but very different in its behaviour; its resistance to crushing and improved moisture resistance is probably the most obvious.

More modern (Second World War to the present) buildings use bricks made to a variety of formulas based on concrete or calcium/alumino-silicates. These can have very different characteristics from traditional clay bricks, which means that they may absorb more/less moisture, depending on the precise composition of the material.

Think carefully before mixing combinations of materials in repairs or extensions.

Mortar

Portland cement was not so common until after the Second World War so most mortar joints up to about 1939 would probably be lime-based.

Lime mortar and Portland cement-based mortar do broadly the same job, but have very different characteristics. Unfortunately this is frequently ignored by specifiers, those supervising the job and even more by builders or their subcontracted plasterers or bricklayers, who seem determined only to use Portland cement mortar either for renders or for brick jointing and bedding or subsequent re-pointing.

Please be very clear: the effect of using the wrong type of mortar can be disastrous, though the reasons behind it are often not acknowledged.

Older walls of soft clay brick tend to absorb rainwater and atmospheric moisture. The old lime mortar joints did too. The ability of these materials to absorb moisture meant they also would lose it fairly readily.

A 215-mm (9-inch) solid brick wall might not be as water resistant as a modern cavity wall under exposed conditions, but it would dry out again if left alone. At least, it probably would until touched by a repair in Portland cement mortar!

Portland cement mortar is a much denser material and retains water content, for example, trapping it in the lime mortar joints behind new re-pointing work or where render had been applied over an entire wall surface.

Being dense, the Portland mortars and renders are prone to 'map pattern' shrinkage cracking – hairline cracks then absorb more moisture through capillary action and make the problem worse. Cracking is initially caused by the dense Portland render and its tendency to shrink back. It does not have the plasticity of the traditional limes, so any water absorbed will freeze in winter, expand, and then shatter the cement.

You will no doubt have seen a wall of soft red brick which has been beautifully re-pointed in a modern Portland mortar – and a good proportion of the bricks will be showing a bright red/orange where the face has blown away due to winter frost action. The old joints might well have been weathered, but the brick had probably survived intact for well over 100 years until it was repaired!

Stone walls can be similarly damaged by incorrect repairs.

Some builders like to point out the inadequacies of the underfired old soft red bricks which have 'become porous' – ignoring the fact that they had survived perfectly well until the re-pointing works were done.

Portland cement has its place. It cures quickly compared with some limes (although modern lime formulations are now surprisingly quick curing) and the adhesive qualities are normally well in excess of those achieved in lime mortar. Portland mortar does set in a very rigid joint and does not accommodate building movements well.

Portland cement pointing on an old wall

But the golden rule is:

where there is original lime render or pointing, it is appropriate – in most cases – to repair like-for-like.

Render

As with mortar, render coats are likely to trigger defects due to moisture ingress. Portland renders are commonly applied to 'weatherproof' a wall but have the reverse effect because moisture becomes trapped behind the render layer within the solid wall. Even where render is applied to a modern cavity wall, some care needs to be taken with use of appropriately gauged and mixed mortar layers.

Nine times out of 10, mortar has never been properly graded or the appropriate number of coats set. Dense single coat render is likely to lead to shrinkage cracking, moisture ingress (and frost damage then blowing off the render) and so on. Use of Portland-cement-rich renders (often applied in only one coat to a wall) can rapidly lead to differential thermal expansion, when compared with the rate of movement of the wall behind. Any hairline cracking can then encourage capillary action to draw moisture into the wall (rainwater running down the face of the wall etc.), accelerating deterioration and eventually blowing the mortar away from the wall (frost action damage).

On the other hand, renders can also be a sensible way to dress and clean up a wall where the cosmetic finish to the brickwork is now beyond help.

There are some 'key' items to remember:

- Sufficient key needs to be left on the surface of the wall for the mortar to adhere to.

- Renders need to be built up in appropriately gauged coats, becoming progressively courser towards the outer face of the wall in order to help control the passage of moisture through the wall and to accommodate some movement in the render itself.

- Guidance is set out in the Approved Document section of the Building Regulations (Approved Document C – Section 5.9). This is explained in further detail in British Standard EN998-1:2003 and in the British Standard 5262:1991 *Code of Practice for External Renderings*). This is no longer a current British Standard but nevertheless is the version cited in the Building Regulations and continues to set out good advice.

- Even on new work use of a traditional lime mortar rather than Portland cement base is well worth considering, because it is much less prone to shrinkage and cracking. Not all limes are 'traditional' and there are modern formulations which set much quicker than the historic mixes.

- Further advice is available in the British Standards and from websites sponsored by organisations such as The Lime Centre near Twyford, Hants (*www.thelimecentre.co.uk*) and Hampshire Building Preservation Trust, Bursledon Brickworks (*www.hampshirebuildings.org.uk/bursledon-brickworks.htm*).

A typical scenario for lime rendering on an older building – for example to replace a section of defective or mismatched render (perhaps where Portland is being used in place of lime where original rendering is already in lime) is given in Problem 9.15 Weathered or desiccated mortar joints.

Mortars and renders – mix guides

The Building Regulations 2000 (Materials and Workmanship Approved Document to support Regulation 7) and British Standards both set out appropriate Codes of Practice for mortars and renders: BS 8000-3:1989 *Workmanship on building sites. Code of Practice for masonry*, AMD 6195 1990; and BS 8000-10:1995 *Workmanship on building sites. Code of Practice for plastering and rendering*, AMD 9271 1996.

PRELIMINARY CHECKS

Defects in general – and wall defects in particular – should not be considered in isolation, otherwise there is a risk of treating only a part of the problem rather than the whole.

When making a preliminary assessment, you should bear in mind the advice in texts on building surveys in deciding the extent of the problem. There are two main elements to consider at this stage:

- structural stability
- the wall fabric in more general terms.

Structural stability

Structural stability will either be:

- immediately dangerous – affecting the safety of the building and its occupants
- a progressive defect such as subsidence (can be very difficult to distinguish from, say, old settlement or shrinkage).

Dangerous structures

Under Sections 77 and 78 of The Building Act 1984, the local authority can require the owner of a dangerous structure to make it safe or, in an emergency, the authority can take direct action to remove the danger.

It can be very difficult to form a sensible view of whether a building is 'dangerous', though I would advise all readers to err on the side of caution. If in doubt, a second opinion, or even a third, can save much embarrassment. Luckily, many Building Control Officers will be in a position to assist if there is a possibility of a Dangerous Structures Notice being issued.

A Dangerous Structures Notice can apply to parts of buildings as well as whole structures.

Building Control Officers have powers (and a duty) under Sections 77 or 78 of the Building Act 1984 to enforce appropriate action.

Dangerous Structures Notice and procedure

1. Inspect the building. Does it 'pass' or 'fail' simple tests such as:
   - ☐ excessive bulging
   - ☐ loose masonry
   - ☐ walls displaced by more than one-third of their thickness
   - ☐ 'significant' cracks (i.e. cracks that are 15–25 mm or greater than 25 mm in width)
   - ☐ fresh/recent cracks.
2. If you are unsure of the safety of the wall, seek a second opinion (i.e. Structural Engineer).
3. Public safety is paramount. Liaise with Building Control; urgent actions might include:
   - ☐ demolition
   - ☐ repair
   - ☐ temporary support.
4. Check the situation with the building's insurers
5. Check with owners/leaseholders/neighbours and any other interested parties. NB: Are there any Party Wall issues?
6. If the situation is not life-threatening, and works are non-urgent, agree a programme of works within the timescales set out in the Building Act 1984, Section 80 (Demolition Notice) (some minor works are exempt if demolition *is* required).
7. Give adequate – usually six weeks – notice to: gas and electric services if demolishing.

In less extreme cases there are some simple tests to help you arrive at a decision:

- Carefully thump the wall with the palm of your hand. (Think about where you are standing before you do this!)
- A garden wall could be carefully rocked to test the condition of the mortar bonding (it is frightening how many can be readily flexed). Even enclosing walls in a building can sometimes be felt to flex when they are in poor condition and the mortar bond/adhesion is no longer effective.
- Measure the amount of distortion or leaning out of plumb. Forget plumb bobs! Use of a long spirit level (minimum 1200 mm), with the gap measured at one end by a steel rule, is a very useful thing to know.

For measurements, the rule of thumb is the rule of thirds:

If the wall leans out by one third of its thickness, it is fair to assume the load path through the wall is not stable and the structural integrity of the wall is likely to be prejudiced.

Another option is sighting down the horizontal mortar course joints. This can give a good indication of how much the wall may have bellied-out or sunk locally – perhaps due to made ground, local soft spots, or localised overloading. The latter is not always fatal to a building and is common in properties built up to about 1940. Wide windows with narrow brick piers in between mean that building loads are concentrating onto fairly narrow sections of wall or onto the Party Walls, causing a recognisable pattern of distortion.

You should also consider whether the building has been constructed 'uniformly'. It is not uncommon for gables in older properties to be formed in only half brick skins 100 mm (4 inches) thick when the rest of the building is in cavity masonry construction. The gable frequently fails, perhaps under wind suction, and starts to lean out before eventually collapsing. This was a common feature following the storms of the late 1980s, when many masonry gables collapsed.

Measurement in these locations can be difficult, so you must be prepared do some serious crawling through the roof space if necessary.

Monitoring using a precision-engineering level may be appropriate in some cases to decide if movement is seasonal. Insurers will generally be involved where trees

Broken flank wall, caused by overloading adjacent to the front door

and shrinkable soils have created a problem and where the foundations have inadequate depth. The insurer may also drive the repair solution.

> **Be careful – today's partial underpinning can be tomorrow's negligence claim, and many engineering practices are issuing much more robust advice and repair strategies than perhaps they did 15 or 20 years ago.**

There was a time when a localised repair followed by a wait-and-see approach was considered appropriate, and generally managed to limit the expenditure on repairs. Litigious times have largely done away with this, however, and Building Owners or their insurers now tend to insist on a final repairs solution which may demand some over-engineering.

Stability issues – common problems

- **Insufficiently tied-in building elements** – particularly (but not exclusively) when dealing with older properties. Floors, for example, provide a considerable proportion of the rigidity and bracing to the structure.
- **Bowing or rippling to the walls** – always warrants further investigation to establish how well the joists

are tied in to the wall fabric in both directions. It is not uncommon to find houses, perhaps built in the 1920s and 1930s, which have joist spans running parallel with the front and rear walls in a terrace. At this time, window openings were becoming larger, perhaps with French casements at the back of the property. Consequently the loads are concentrated in quite narrow bands of brick piers, particularly at the rear of the building, and there is no structural tie-in from front to rear, with the consequence that walls start to bulge and lean outwards.

- **Quality of masonry bonding** – bonding for masonry partition walls and load-bearing walls within the building can be of dubious quality. Sometimes there is little more than a butted-up joint with no meaningful toothing-in of the brickwork to lock the structure together between external main walls and load-bearing masonry partitions. Where significant distortions are involved, it may be necessary to strip out some of the internal surface and plaster finishes in order to arrive at a robust conclusion about the extent of repairs required, and this is unlikely to have been investigated within the remit of a normal condition survey.

It is always a temptation to cause the minimum amount of disturbance, particularly in residential properties where an investigation can cause some distress to the occupants. However, better by far to come up with the right solution even if it does mean creating something of a mess to arrive at that conclusion.

If the structure is not dangerous, you need to form a view as to whether the problem is going to get worse or not.

Assuming the building does not qualify for a major repair, you will need to consider and discuss the following with the client:

- The economic life that the building has to fulfil (will it be demolished, altered, extended or disposed of in the foreseeable future?). (Prioritise this against any other repairs.)
- Is there a maintenance programme or budget to consider?
- Is the defect wear-and-tear, or is it subject – at least potentially – to an insurance claim.
- Are there any statutory issues (such as Listed Building status, public buildings with a health and safety requirement, disabled access) that need to be incorporated within the repairs advice.

All of these (and probably some other factors besides) will influence the repairs strategy, and the timing and type and cost of repairs carried out.

PROBLEMS – WALLS

9.1 JOINING NEW WALLS TO OLD

There are two key considerations when a new wall is to be joined to an existing wall (perhaps for an extension):

- Will the contractor use a modern metric brick and tooth it into older imperial gauge brickwork? (This often looks unsightly because the new bricks are tipped and angled to fit into the existing mortar courses and the join becomes conspicuous.)
- Is there any risk of even quite minor building movement between the new extension settling down and the pre-existing structure? If so, then any toothing in may well result in the tooth bricks cracking or snapping across the abutment joint or the joint pulling open.

Solution 1

Using metal connector plates generally provides a neat solution in most circumstances (see Solution 2). The plate is bolted to the wall at the join line and metal wall ties are locked in at the appropriate intervals to bond in the new work to the old existing structure. Even if the courses are mismatched, at least there is a relatively neat butt joint.

It is advisable to inset the new work slightly from the face of the old wall to provide a relief angle or shadow line which can mask any relatively minor imperfections and create a more pleasing transition from old to new.

Solution 2

In the case of a historic building it may well be better to spend more on imperial gauge bricks and go for a carefully toothed-in join. Or perhaps address the problem by setting the new wall back further from the face of the old to provide a larger shadow line to help conceal the joint. When all else fails, concealing the joint behind a rainwater downpipe has its attractions!

9.2 CRACKING IN MORTAR JOINTS (SAND-BASED AND OTHER BRICK TYPES)

Following the widespread use of calcium silicate and alumino-silicate-based bricks in the 1960s and 1970s, it is common to see cracks in mortar, often coupled with inadequate movement joints. Significant expansion cracking is frequently apparent.

Solution

Cutting in new expansion joints (and reinforcing the reveals with extra wall ties) is usually the only economic answer. Generally buildings which incorporate this type of brick were originally built to a budget and are unlikely to warrant an expensive cosmetic treatment.

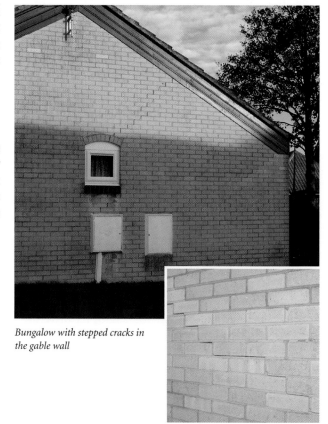

Bungalow with stepped cracks in the gable wall

COST SEQUENCE – Cutting-in expansion joint to cavity wall outer leaf

1. Assumed wall height to 2 storeys/5 metres.
2. Determine position for retro-fit wall tie reinforcement prior to cutting expansion joint chase within wall. Install wall ties on either side of intended expansion joint chase at double the British Standard vertical centres, i.e. nominally 225 mm centres; and if using a proprietary wall tie remedial system allow for drilling through vertical centre of brick in accordance with manufacturer's instructions to tap or grout wall ties to inner then external face of wall.
3. Allow for careful re-pointing in colour mortar to the face of the brick. When wall reinforcing ties have been installed, with grout properly cured, then expansion joint cutting may commence.
4. Fix timber batten to wall and check for plumb along position for expansion joint.
5. Provide adequate working access/scaffold tower or appropriate platform.
6. Using 110-volt chasing saw set to appropriate depth (slightly in excess of combined batten depth and brick depth) follow line of batten to cut chase to wall.
7. Re-locate batten and repeat process to cut second kerf to create expansion joint of nominal width, say 15 mm, or as required.
8. Fit stainless steel expansion ties in sliding plastic sleeves grouted in epoxy-modified cement mortar at, say 450 mm, nominal vertical centres and across the newly formed joint. Face-point the joint to match existing/surrounding finish. Set the ties in at the centre of the face brick depth. Install compressible fill in the expansion joint and face-up with mastic, if required.

Cutting in expansion joint to cavity wall outer leaf – COST £950

9.3 DPC WALL OVER-SAIL

Stepped cracking and over-sailing of the wall, which then hangs out above the DPC line and the wall beneath (which is restrained by the ground around the foundations), is still commonly seen in all types of masonry.

You need to be aware of the problems this can cause and refer to brick design tables (such as those in the Building Regulations Approved Document A, Section 2C, or published by the Brick Development Association at *www.brick.org.uk*) for guidance on how to help prevent this.

However, the problem is not confined to shrinkable silicate-type bricks, and any clay brick as well as concrete or composition bricks will be prone to movement, thermal expansion and some initial moisture-induced dimensional changes.

It is not uncommon for building designers under pressure to supply only minimal information on working drawings, leaving a window open for considerable interpretation on site. The results are not always favourable – insufficient tying-in being a typical occurance.

Solution

In long walls, expansion joints should be considered. Sometimes expansion joints will also be needed in short walls if the material is particularly prone to shrinkage/movement.

In both cases, appropriate detailing (extra wall ties) around doors and windows and expansion joints are essential.

Expansion joints are not pretty, but they can be recessed if necessary by a return in the wall line (often an ideal place to position the rainwater downpipe to hide the fibre or mastic strip sealing the expansion joint).

Over-sail above the DPC

9.4 DEFECTIVE WALL TIES

Wall tie failure is a very common problem on many older properties – visibly apparent from the horizontal mortar joint cracks at wall tie bedding intervals.

Cast iron or steel bars were commonly employed to brace the leaves of cavity construction, though not exclusively so, and there are many other types of wall tie which have been in use over the last century or more. For example, cranked, ceramic glazed ties are prone to lack of mortar adhesion, particularly where lime mortars have been used and where the glazed surface of the tie might cause very poor bonding.

The iron ties, if they were ever galvanised, will have a finite lifespan. (Some were dipped in bitumen, some galvanised, others not at all.) As these deteriorate, the iron ties are prone to delaminate, causing a significant expansion within the bedding joint of the wall and a telltale pattern of horizontal cracks at about 450 mm (18 inch) centres appears.

This usually manifests itself first around door and window openings where the pressure and loading around the tie is less.

However, a pattern is not always visible. Occasionally you may come across a substandard house with perhaps only one tie on one wall! Although this defies the laws of physics to some extent, it is surprising how many buildings have stood the test of time with only minimal bracing of this kind.

Although building age is a reasonable indicator of when cavity wall ties might have been employed, in some parts of the country they were used much earlier than in others. For example, in parts of the south coast, wall ties were commonly used in buildings dating from about 1870, whereas they only became common in parts of London or north Surrey from the 1920s.

The case of the waving wall
Using a metal detector to locate the old wall ties is useful, but does not guarantee results.

About 20 years ago, I had to carry out an inspection on an old hotel on the south coast, where ceramic wall ties had been used and so of course a metal detector was of limited value. The wall was a substantial one, and the external face of the wall had pulled away from the wall ties under wind suction. The ceramic wall ties had then dropped down within the cavity, and when the wind suction dropped, the wall could no longer return to its original position because it was blocked by the wall ties.

The wall was actually rippling under the wind load. A rebuilding operation ensued, requiring substantial scaffolding (and cleaning and re-use of the bricks on what was a Listed Building).

The expense was considerable. A preventative maintenance programme might have picked up this detail, so that remedial wall ties could have been fitted before the defect progressed to this costly state of affairs.

Solution

Wall ties are probably one of the easier repairs to implement. There are various proprietary systems on the market including an expanding Rawl-bolt pattern, and a stainless steel helical bar which is driven into the centre of the brick, cutting a thread and self-tapping into the masonry as it is inserted.

Crudely repaired using mastic – an expansion 'joint' has 'developed' on a long factory wall, where none was allowed for in the construction!

Most of these systems use an injected polyester resin in order to provide additional adhesion into the internal skin brick, and particularly on the external brick skin where the act of inserting the tie is likely to have reamed-out the insertion hole, providing a less tight fit unless some form of glue is applied.

Before proceeding, however, you should check the following:

- **Is it a cavity wall** – Sometimes a solid wall with a stretcher bond can be mistaken for a cavity wall (an old 13-inch wall, for example). If there is no door or window reveal to check wall thickness, then you should carefully probe the wall.
- **The condition of the mortar jointing to the wall** – Occasionally the mortar bond will have desiccated so far that even if the wall ties are repaired the condition of the bonding and adhesion in the mortar is so poor it may in fact prove easier to reconstruct the external skin of the wall (commonly seen in ancient lime mortars).
- **Which leaf of the cavity wall is load-bearing** – Although good building practice and long-established tradition suggests that the inner leaf should always be load-bearing, on some older properties the roof and wall plate may bear down on the external leaf. A quick check beforehand will establish if any additional means of support are required before laying into the external leaf of the wall and potentially removing the support.

Other options

On a 13-inch solid wall, it is not uncommon for the facing brick to bulge away from the 215-mm (9-inch) wall beneath. If not too severe, the face brickwork can be pinned back using the helical remedial tie system mentioned above. There is a grout offered as part of this proprietary system to assist with bonding back together.

Please note:

- Usual practice is to install the new remedial wall ties first before then isolating the old wall ties to reduce attrition to what may be a very tired wall bond.
- Isolation can sometimes be done by using a needle gun to expose the end of the tie before coating it in polyurethane foam to insulate it from moisture and prevent any excessive further rusting. But it would be preferable to completely isolate the end of the tie from the outside wall and prevent further expansion and pressure on the brickwork (which, if allowed to continue unchecked, can cause a pattern of rippling and bulging to the wall and eventually might lead to collapse, although few properties ever reach that stage of deterioration).
- When the masonry panel has been re-secured using the new ties, it is then safer and easier to remove bricks adjacent to each rusting and defective wall tie, and bend the defective tie end down within the cavity. It is then no longer bedded into the masonry, where it might continue to rust, expand and distort the wall.

COST SEQUENCE – Wall ties

- Specification based on a single elevation wall; 10 m in length and 2 storeys high, with gable, and with 3 window openings and 1 door opening.
- Assumes owner/occupier supplies power.
- Assumes all areas are accessible with no special access required, e.g. to bridge-over conservatories, outbuildings or other projections which could make working dangerous or add significantly to access costs.
- Use of a helical tie is assumed in this instance.
- Contractor to supply access, e.g. scaffold tower, to enable safe working access to upper limits of wall.

1. Install new helical wall ties by drilling to centre of brick at 450 mm vertical centres and 900 mm horizontal centres with double density ties to reveals around door and window openings, and all works in accordance with British Standards, including wall tie densities.
2. Ensure ties are soundly bonded by self-tapping, and use of resin fixing to both inner and outer skins of wall.
3. When all new ties are stabilised and fixed, then allow for careful break out of individual bricks to enable old, defective and rusting ties to be removed/isolated by bending down from the outer leaf within the cavity of the wall. Wall ties to remain fixed to the inner leaf.

4. Re-insert and point-in brick where defective wall ties have been removed. Allow for 100% breakages and matching in of new brick to existing – assumes a common brick stock such as a London red brick or similar.
5. Allow for removal of bricks above damp-proof course level at 1.5 m centres and raking out using bent pipe or similar to remove any slovens or debris which may have dropped to the bottom of the cavity, to clear the cavity and ensure damp-proof course operates effectively.
6. Reinstate where brick is removed. Assumes 100% breakages to all brick openings. Allow for matching basic specification brick as detailed above.
7. On completion of all works, clear away all scaffold and debris and arisings.
8. Allow for re-pointing only in areas where new bricks have been inserted with no re-pointing to the main wall area.
9. Allow for coloured mortar mix to re-point the face of brick where new wall ties have been drilled through.

Wall ties – COST £3,500

9.5 WALL BOWING

Bowing and distortion to walls can occur for a variety of reasons:

- overloading of the wall because of modern concrete tiles being used on the roof instead of slate (as per the original specification), upsetting the equilibrium of a building which was otherwise previously performing satisfactorily
- lack of adequate restraint and bracing to the wall
- collapsing arches over windows or doorways
- soft spots in the ground where the foundations have inadequate bearing so that the wall may have rotated slightly on the foundation causing bulging further up the structure as it deforms
- poor original building materials
- 'external influences' such as shockwave damage from Second World War or other bombing incidents
- solar overheating of a wall without expansion joints.

Solution 1

If the problem is caused by solar overheating, a solar reflective or light toned paint may assist if the problem is slight.

In addition to any other repairs that might be needed, it is appropriate to tie back the wall, provided the degree of distortion is within acceptable limits (extra wall ties or tie-in to the joists).

However, be aware that over-restraint elsewhere risks making the problem worse. For example, rebuilding sections of the wall using an overly strong Portland cement mix in the mortar would constrain the ability of the wall to move and might make distortions worse in weaker areas adjoining the repair.

Solution 2

Traditionally the remedy for a bowing wall is to use restraining bars or tie bars with the classic iron or steel crosses or discs acting as spreader plates visible on the external part of the wall – helping spread the load of the restraining bar which was subsequently run over the top of the floor joists (notched into them) and fixed down beneath the floor covering.

When carrying out this type of exercise it is particularly important to ensure that adequate restraint is placed across the floor, e.g. using timber noggings so that the joists are not prone to buckling across their width.

The traditional tie bar is a useful way of restraining the wall and certainly the spreading plates across the surface of the wall can spread the point load picked up from the restraining bar over a considerable area. However, they are somewhat unsightly, and some other more discrete methods of restraining the wall are now available.

Solution 3

Stainless steel helical bars similar to the wall ties mentioned above can be used to stitch the wall and effectively attach it by penetrating the wall at a number of locations and spearing through the joists. Again, some form of nogging is essential to prevent the joists buckling and deforming sideways, but a cosmetically improved restraint can be put in place (when compared with the traditional tie bar) with significantly improved rigidity across the wall.

It is also well worth considering use of galvanised steel straps fitted across notches within the joists where they run parallel with the distorted wall and strapped over nogging pieces and screw fixed to the inside leaf of the wall which, coupled with wall tie repairs, can provide some significant additional bracing.

A variety of systems have been produced by Helifix Limited, and the figure below illustrates the range of applications.

The use of polyester resin glue is generally essential when using stainless steel helix solutions; it provides an amazing amount of adhesion in order to glue together fixings and masonry finishes.

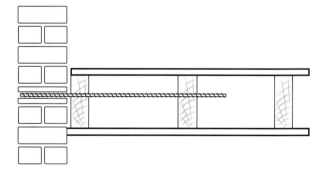

COST SEQUENCE – Installation of helical fixing wall anchor to secure bowing wall

- Assumes that wall anchors will be inserted at the first floor joist level.
- Contractor to supply scaffold tower or equivalent safe working access.
- Assumes that the elevation of the building being treated is not obstructed by any unusual hazards or building projections with no special access requirements resulting from this.
- Specification assumes 4 stainless steel helical anchor bars are drilled through from the external face of the wall at 1m centres.

1. Take up floorboards internally and carefully set aside for re-use.

2. Install noggings/blocking pieces to the voids between 3 sets of joists running parallel with the wall: 3 noggins per void (9 in total).

- Assumes that the helical tie bars will be positioned to miss any services and that no re-routing of electrical or pipe work is required.
- Ensure the helical tie bars pass through the stiffened joist sections.

3. Re-point face of wall where the helical bar has been drilled through and secured with resin bonding.

4. Re-instate floorboards, screwed back down into place.

Wall anchors – COST £400

9.6 HISTORIC CRACKS

When assessing the cause of cracks it is essential to adopt a 'holistic' approach – that is to say, view the crack as part of the whole building. For instance, are parts of the building over-loaded down narrow masonry load paths (brick piers)? Or could the orientation of the building be causing wind suction or thermal expansion cracking on exposed southern/western aspects?

Note: Using 'telltales' to check whether a crack is ongoing is not always effective. Other options include resin-fixed screws around a crack (three screws) measured, say, monthly using a vernier gauge can provide you with increments of vertical and lateral displacement across two planes. A spirit level can be used to provide a third measure of lateral displacement, but the accuracy may be limited unless there is room to use a long spirit level across the wall or the movement becomes very dramatic.

Solution 1 – Brick slips

Carefully cutting a matching brick to create a slip which can be glued in place across a cracked brick is probably the neatest way of repairing a damaged brick. The old damaged section needs to be carefully chased back, perhaps by partly drilling away. A matching mortar can be used to secure new to old. Use of a resin glue behind the slip is feasible if you are reasonably confident water will not be retained as a result.

Sometimes it is possible to use an old brick from a sacrificial part of the building. (For example, if you are carrying out alteration works, then some careful salvage may pay dividends.)

Solution 2 – Coloured mortar

This can provide a neat match but is really only suitable for small areas of repair; used over larger spans, colouring differences can start to show through, possibly later on as the mortar weathers.

Solution 3 – Stitch-in repairs

Sometimes there is no alternative but to construct a whole new section of masonry let in as a repair.

Every endeavour should be made to match the brick finish and composition and mortar jointing, and also to coordinate the brick sizes.

Differences between metric and imperial bricks may be small, but hopefully the repair will be there to look at for a long time, and a poor match can look disastrous and piecemeal. Several patch-in repairs can soon spoil the look of the entire building.

9.7 'LIVE' CRACKS CAUSED BY LINTEL FAILURE/DROPPED ARCH

If the movement is ongoing, the structure needs to be stabilised before proceeding. A temporary support – screwjacks or raking shores/buttresses if appropriate – should be adequate for most circumstances.

If the problem has arisen because the soldier course has dropped or the keystone pointing has weathered away, it is usually easy to repair. Adequate and safe access may be the greatest difficulty for working at height.

Check that the arch finishes at the wall reveals, as it was designed to do. It is not uncommon to find someone has previously widened the opening to ease in a wider window or door salvaged from elsewhere. If so, the arch may not be repairable without rebuilding the reveals to support the side thrust from the arch.

Check the condition of a timber backing lintel if there is one. If decayed by contact with damp solid wall surfaces, then replacement with a modern steel box lintel or reinforced concrete (RC) lintel behind the facework arch may be more appropriate.

Solution 1

Temporary support will be needed – a cantilevered screwjack is probably most convenient in this instance, located within the building and set into the wall from the inside face to support and take up the load temporarily while work is being completed. If working on timber floors the screwjacks will need adequate support and a load path down to something solid, or use timber load spreading plates.

An engineering calculation would be appropriate if floor joists are in very poor condition (or you may need a temporary working scaffold both inside and outside the structure).

It should prove fairly simple to deconstruct some or all of the arch once the floor and wall load has been relieved. The arch can then be rebuilt using a timber former. If the bricks have been 'rubbed' and set to a tapering gauge, then, if they cannot be salvaged, rubbing in new brick is comparatively simple for a skilled bricklayer, but will necessarily add to the time and cost.

Once the mortar has set, supports can be struck.

Solution 2

Stainless steel helical bars offer a couple of repair options:

- The bars can be embedded in the mortar courses at vertical intervals and secured in an epoxy-modified mortar within the joint before remaking the face pointing to match the original. This helps to create a beam across the top of the arch and relieve the load permanently so that the brick detail does not have to work quite so hard in the future.
- As a further measure, the brick or stone arch can be drilled at an angle and helical bars skewed into the masonry and glued in with an epoxy or polyester resin to physically lock the bricks together. This is especially useful if the arch has not yet failed, but will need re-pointing, and there is a risk of further mortar dropping out and the arch sagging during the work.

COST SEQUENCE – Dropped/depressed brick window/door arch

1. Provide temporary support to depressed arch using, e.g., screw jack with profiled timber former beneath the arch/soffit.
2. Carefully chase out the mortar courses above the brick arch using an electrician's bolster/chasing bolster or similar. Allow for chasing 2 courses in the horizontal bed joints, separated by 2 courses depth above the arch.
3. Chase the depth to about one third/half bed joint.
4. Carefully brush out and wet the chases. Using epoxy resin-modified mortar, prepare the back of the joint. Install helical stainless steel reinforcing bar to each joint and re-grout and finish point each chase.
5. Extend the chases nominally 300 mm beyond each side of the brick arch. (Large spans might need more.)
6. Jack the brick arch into position once the helical fixings have formed a relieving arch above the brick arch. Carefully break out and chase away any loose mortar. Wet out joints and re-grout. Fair finish/re-point the wall to match the existing/original style of pointing.
7. When all grouting has cured and masonry is secured by adhesion, then allow for drilling in of, say, 8 helical bars to be skew-fixed through the arch to provide additional mechanical fixing. Allow for coloured-in pointing to the face of the brick to re-secure and provide re-cosmetic finish and prevent entry of water to masonry.

Dropped/depressed brick window/door arch – COST £480

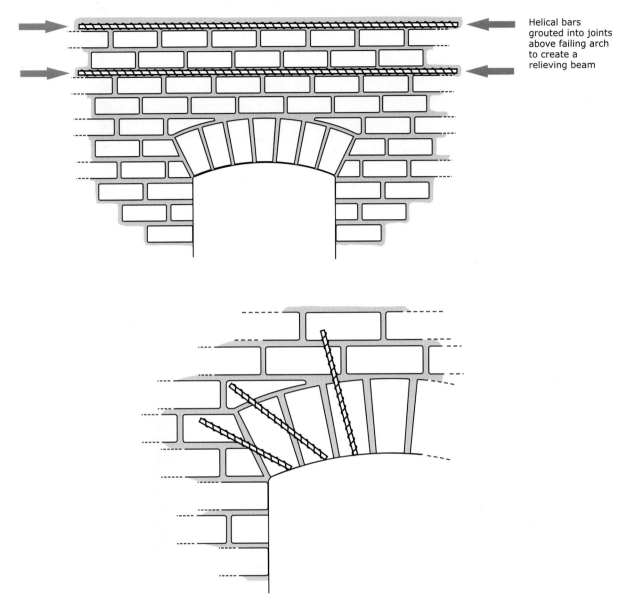

Helical bars grouted into joints above failing arch to create a relieving beam

Helical bars could be used to mechanically fix a dropped brick arch.

9.8 DEFECTIVE FLAT ARCH

The two most common causes of flat lintel failure are:

- failure of the reinforcing bar in an RC lintel
- corroded or inadequate end bearings in a steel boot lintel (the usual minimum bearing being 150 mm).

If the end bearings are corroded, then temporary alleviation can sometimes be achieved by cleaning off rust and expanded oxidised steel from the bearing ends with a needle gun, before repainting the metal. Eventually, however, the corrosion will re-assert itself and the lintel will ultimately fail.

If the spot welds have started to fail, a helical relieving beam in the masonry above (if there is room) may be feasible for short term effect; likewise if the end bearing is inadequate (frequently they are as little as 80 mm). Internally the dry-lining always seems to take care of this on new construction work and nicely masks everything. But you should advise your client that the unit will need to be replaced in the foreseeable future if a reduced end-bearing is confirmed (usually the result of sloppy site work).

Solution 1 (temporary): defective RC lintels

If not too severely affected, the concrete can be rebuilt around the 'remet' bar.

The steel bar has to be cleaned down and stabilised with a treatment to make the surface inert, before rebuilding the face in an epoxy-modified mortar.

Sometimes an anode can be built in by a specialist remedial contractor, as a retrofit measure. This anode will reduce the future effects of galvanic corrosion of the steel which may be a problem, for example, in an aggressive marine climate.

Note: if a lintel that has insufficient concrete cover over the bar is then repaired, this will extend its life, but nevertheless it will one day need replacement.

If you have to replace the lintel with a like-for-like new RC lintel you must allow for reconstruction of at least three courses of new brickwork above, plus (probably) a complete new damp proof tray and cloaking detail.

Solution 2: Steel boot lintel

The steel boot lintel is now ubiquitous and is often specified without a second thought.

Note: the quality of the surface coating can be critical to its application and lifespan.

If you read the manufacturers' 'small print' and guidance, most will advise that the ends of the beams should be painted. Extra paint protection is advised in marine climates; without it the lifespan can be as little as 40 years or so before the bearing ends deteriorate. Most buildings have a 60-year life-span when designed (and in practice may last 100 years or more), so precautionary works to extend the life of components

is sensible – and cheap if done during the original construction, when compared with the cost of a later repair.

Solution 3: Crack stitching

If the cause of the problem can be arrested, then the helicals can be set along the joints of the brick or stonework to re-secure the wall fabric across the cracks and spread some of the loads around the weak plane caused by the fracture.

Proprietary systems can help you avoid a rebuild
I have been using a system manufactured by Helifix (*www.helifix.co.uk*) for about 20 years, but it seems to have found favour with engineers more than surveyors (who, in my experience, seem to prefer rebuilding things).

In fact, I have even been involved in one or two legal disputes where the judge was persuaded that the system effectively was 'new fangled' and awarded on the basis of rebuilding rather than repair!

The Helifix specifiers' manual provides methods statements for various repair scenarios, and the company offers access to a technical and engineering service to prove repairs/loads, so further variations on the theme are not repeated here.

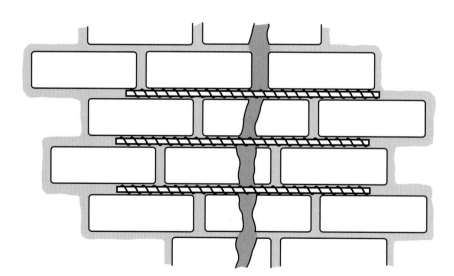

Insert helical ties to reinforce a poor-quality masonry bond or to stitch across a crack/fissure.

9.9 TEMPORARY SUPPORT OF WALLS

Details of calculations for the temporary support of vertical wall loads and working practices are set out in the excellent BRE Good Building Guides (available from *www.brebookshop.com*):

- GBG10 *Temporary support for openings in external wall: assessing loads* (1992)
- GBG 15 *Providing temporary support during work on openings in external walls* (1992)
- GBG 20 *Removing internal loadbearing walls in older dwellings* (1999).

Needles or timber beams run through the wall and supporting the section above the area about to be repaired are normally fixed through the wall at 1 m centres – but be careful if the wall is an old one and the bonding between the bricks is too poor even to allow needling.

Cantilevered screw jacks reduce the need to support from both sides of the wall and improve working access. But you or the builder should double-check the load being applied to the jack to assess whether it is within safe working tolerances.

If it is a solid wall, you may be able to use steel channels to build up the lintel in two sections by supporting half the thickness of the wall and sliding in the channel section from each side, then bolting them together through the web. However, this requires very clean working to prevent debris falling into the joint.

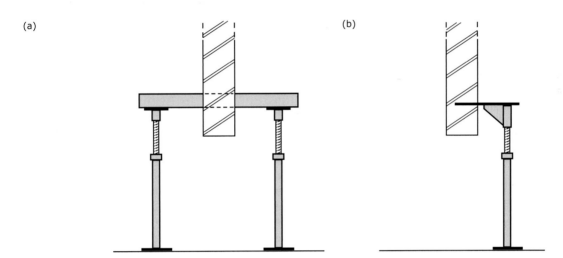

(a)

(b)

Temporary supports to walls: (a) Traditional 'needle' through support on screw jacks – reduces working access; load is spread across two points;
(b) Cantilevered screw jack may provide much better access – vital to check that the wall above is well bonded and unlikely to buckle; check bearing for the prop (load concentrated in a small area).

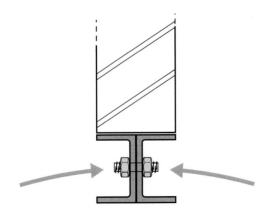

Use of two steel channels to form a single beam, where working access or support proves difficult.

9.10 DISTORTION AND/OR CRACKS DUE TO FOUNDATION FAILURE

The majority of foundation failures in older buildings are probably caused by either drains failure or subsequent changes in soil volume water demand resulting from tree and vegetation planting since the building was constructed.

Underpinning – considered by some to be one of those black arts requiring a very specialist design – may not be necessary, providing you look carefully for the clues as to any likely cause.

However, if the building is in an area that is subject to issues such as mining subsidence, or if there are 'water solution features' – that is to say, big holes caused by washing out due to prevailing limestone and underground water courses or similar – then specialist solutions beyond the scope of this book may well apply.

If you decide to proceed, consider carefully whether there is any likelihood of the building being locked into place in one section with foundations free to float elsewhere. This can be a problem on shrinkable clay soils where further stress cracking can occur once part of the building is set on a rigid foundation, when other previously unnoticed movements suddenly become apparent as the building 'floats' up and down.

Insurance companies have historically been extremely keen to minimise cost exposure by only underpinning partial elements of the building, but the client needs to be aware that this can cause further distress to the structure.

There has been an increasing trend recently for engineers to recommend underpinning of the whole building to avoid this, but circumstances vary in individual cases: it will sometimes depend on whether a loss adjuster is involved with a particular insurance company policy. If there is no insurance company involved, then you will have to form a judgement.

Solution

It is paramount to establish the cause of the problem. The first stage is to dig a trial pit and locate the extent of the problem. If drains are the cause, drain survey information will be required, and any leaking pipework will need to be repaired as part of the underpinning work.

The trial pit should establish the depth of the original foundation and should excavate down to sufficient depth to establish a reasonable load-bearing area in the soil. This is a relatively basic operation – when you can't dig any further with ease and the spade is bouncing off the ground then you have probably reached a suitable depth (typically 1–2 m below ground level).

The underpinning bays generally should not exceed 1 m in width (beyond this the wall probably cannot support itself).

If the wall is particularly old with lime mortar in poor condition and the brick bond is not likely to adhere to itself, then some additional support will be required. Use of screw jacks is the most straightforward option.

Note: It can prove extremely difficult to dig sufficient trenching and remove the screw jacks from the holes. In practise I have often found it easier to leave the screw jacks in situ and pour the concrete around them. Although a slight additional expense, the increased speed of working quite often offsets this.

The section of wall to be underpinned needs to be divided into equal bays so that each bay can be dug, filled and pinned up under the wall, leaving sufficient room for the concrete to cure and another bay to be

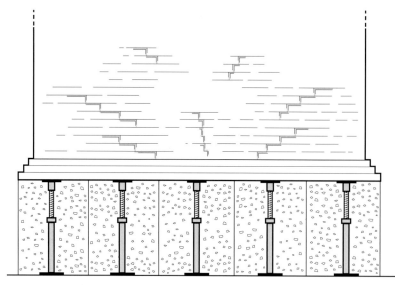

It may prove more economical to cast in the 'temporary' screw jack supports when underpinning: it's quicker; offers assured support to the soffit of the old footing (safety); and the soffit of any footing is forced up so any packing out between the top of the new concrete underpin bay and the underside of old footing can be securely rammed in.

constructed elsewhere. In this way, no section of the wall is unduly weakened at any one time.

Once the concrete has been poured, the remaining gap of about 50–75 mm beneath the soffit of the original foundation should be pinned up by hand using a dry mix, or sometimes a self-expanding mix rammed in.

> **In areas where shrinkable clay soils are a problem, remember to use some form of slip plane such as a folded sheet of damp proof membrane on the outside of the wall to reduce the friction caused by any soil heave which might subsequently occur once underpinning bays are back filled.**
>
> **It is also worth considering the use of stainless steel helical bars bedded into mortar joints to effectively create a reinforced beam along the base of the wall or footing, and assist with spreading load across any localised soft spots, coupled with an underpinning.**

The same technique can be applied when carrying out extension works or modifying existing building layouts:

- It is generally appropriate to excavate and reinforce by underpinning the reveals of any wall openings constructed by breaking through a building – either

---

The benefits of self-expanding cement

In most cases I have used a dry pack self-expanding cement which will fill any voids as it matures and absorbs any natural ground moisture to start the curing process. (Although named 'dry pack' it is in fact rammed in by hand, slightly damp.)

The process is straightforward, providing you consider the steps carefully.

More details for simple domestic low-rise structure underpinning are available in the Building Research Establishment Guide, *Foundation movement and remedial underpinning in low rise buildings.*

I consider any reasonably competent Building Surveyor should be more than capable of designing simple underpinning solutions to typical two-storey domestic structures or their equivalent.

---

removing a load-bearing internal wall or when creating openings into extended sections of the building.

- As the wall is broken open, increased loading or point loading will occur around the newly formed reveals, and even if the original foundations are broadly capable of supporting this, some re-distribution of loads and distress cracking is likely to occur unless the footings are given some more substantial reinforcement.

9.11 EFFLUORESCENCE

Effluorescence is one of the most common causes of staining to masonry.

It generally affects new work rather than being seen on older buildings. The visible white staining occurs when the salts that are within the clay of the brick (or tiles) are dissolved by rainwater and washed to the surface, where they dry.

This may be unsightly, but it is not a significant problem, unless the deposits are at a low level on the elevation, in which case they suggest a failure of the DPC and/or rising ground water (a possible explanation for effluorescence in older buildings).

Solution 1

Increased hosing down and brushing may help accelerate the removal of the salts, but it can take years to eventually disappear.

Solution 2

If a DPC problem is identified, it will be necessary to break out the masonry course and sleeve-in a new DPC membrane.

Effluorescence – in this case salts have crystallised on the wall in an underground tunnel, but the staining can take the form of white chalk-like deposits over the surface of the brick.

9.12 SNOTS

Mortar snots and stains are generally the result of careless repair work. Although some staining is unavoidable, it should be minimal if skilled bricklayers are at work.

Solution

The stains can be removed by careful application of phosphoric acid cleaners and brushing, or using a carborundum stone to lightly grind off the material from the face of the brick.

CAUTION: Suitable protection required – these cleaners are strong acids.

The same technique (using a carborundum block) can be used to rub-in soft bricks to match them into other work or cut in/clean up a simple profile. (However, this is not really a substitute for a proper brick rubbing tool where complex profiles or mouldings need to be cut.)

9.13 BIRD DROPPINGS AND EROSION

Staining from acid rain or from bird droppings can start to cause erosion as well as staining. Limestones can be particularly badly affected in this way.

Solution

Washing down and fitting protective measures such as bird spikes/wires may be the only solution, though you might consider some extra flashing material to protect moulding details from guano or rainwater run-off where feasible.

Vegetation and lichens can also cause deterioration to some stone materials. Insecticides might help, but use of chemical treatments would need to be carefully considered and specialist advice taken, especially if the building is a historic one.

9.14 MASONRY BEES

Bees boring into soft brick or, more likely, mortar joints can cause significant weakening to the joints and fabric if allowed to continue.

Solution

The only answer may be to use an insecticide and to carefully re-point, ensuring that any access points are closed off.

9.15 WEATHERED OR DESICCATED MORTAR JOINTS

Before embarking on re-pointing, it is important to check whether the work is really necessary.

- A small amount of powdery material on the surface of the joint is probably quite acceptable.
- If the joint can be raked fairly easily with a screwdriver or old chisel to, say, half its depth, then re-pointing is an issue.
- If a hammer and bolster or a TCT saw, or similar, is needed to rout out the joint, then frankly the mortar is probably sound enough and is best left alone.

Also, re-pointing should be to a depth of at least twice the thickness of the joint, otherwise the new mortar will never obtain a satisfactory key within the joint. Up to half the depth of the brick is appropriate.

Solution

Do:

- brush out the joint to remove debris
- wet the joint before applying new mortar (to control suction)
- specify for mortar to be pushed into the joint; try to avoid voids(!)
- ensure that suitably sized tools are used to prevent mortar buttering over the face of the brick and ruining the effect – a crime on older buildings especially
- broadly match the mortar types and colour; lime mortar with lime and so on.

Do not:

- allow pointing during periods of heavy rain or frost.

COST SEQUENCE – Lime render

1. Allow for hacking off existing wall surface: assumed elevation is 20 square metres, allowing for window and door penetrations. Take back to sound masonry surface with any loose mortar in brick joints keyed back.
2. Fix pre-formed stainless steel or plastic trims to window hoods, bell-cast to damp-proof course line and any arris beads to reveals of doors, windows and corners of building (first verify if there are to be any 'soft' finishes required consistent with historic buildings, in which case omit the arrises).
3. Wet down working area to control suction.
4. Allow for 3 coats, graded. First coat (strongest mix) not exceeding 16 mm thick. Typically about 10 mm but allow for dubbing to address any irregularities to all surfaces. Apply 2 finishing coats between 6 and 10 mm thick.
5. Allow 2 days' curing time to undercoats during periods of warm weather and one week during wet/inclement weather.
6. Allow for ventilated temporary coverings in polythene sheet or similar to all work, while curing.
7. Allow for spray wetting of wall surfaces to control suction between coats.
8. Allow for wood float finish to final coat and do not over-work.
9. Where carrying out patch repairs, allow for lime wash extra coats at joint between old and new work.
10. *This pricing specification does not allow for any run mouldings.*

Lime render – COST £950

Chapter 10
Roofs and rainwater goods

In the context of the projects relevant to this book, you will probably encounter three main categories of roof:

- modern pre-trussed rafter frame assemblies (sometimes called 'TRADA' roofs)
- traditional 'cut timber' dual pitched (or single pitched lean-to) styles
- flat roofs.

The first two types are most commonly covered with slate, clay tiles or, within the comparatively recent past, concrete tiles. There are numerous other coverings, of course, including various forms of coated sheet steel or other sheet metal. Flat roofs are usually covered in some form of bituminised felt or one of the modern plastic polymer equivalents, but may also employ sheet lead, copper, sheet aluminium and a variety of other materials depending on application.

Less common coverings include:

- asbestos cement and fibre cement slate profiled sheet roof coverings
- profiled/plastic coated metal (PCM) sheet roofs
- built up sheet metal roofs (typically on a timber frame), e.g. sheet copper-slate-covered cupolas.

Other categories of construction, such as the 'cruck' framed roofs in old timber frame structures, or domestic properties with steel roof lattices (such as in the Trusteel™ prefabricated wall and roof design), are beyond the scope of the 'traditional building repairs' discussed in this book.

KEY CONSIDERATIONS

The main question in your mind when approaching a roof repair must always be:

- ◆ **Will the property be mortgageable, once the improvements have been carried out; or is a mortgage valuer likely to consider that the works have compromised the property?**

Having said that, you will probably have to accept that older roofs are unlikely to achieve the standards set by the most recent Building Regulations.

- ◆ **Bear in mind that roof work may often involve tackling a wall that is a party structure. If so, you will need to serve a Party Wall Act notice if the fabric or loading is being modified in any way (see Chapter 7).**

◆ **Adding to the weight of the roof is a structural modification, and under the Building Regulations (Approved Document A) this work needs approval (a Building Notice is usually sufficient).**

When carrying out any roof repair or reinforcement works I would also urge you to:

- check the condition of all the flashings
- check the condition of any timbers such as wall plates or trimmers around chimneys because any minor damp trickling through can cause timbers to badly soften without any telltale mushroom growth to highlight the problem
- check the condition of any fixing nails – if the roof is old, these may have rusted away, and the added weight of roofers and the vibration of repairs could trigger slippage and spreading out of the roof timbers: re-fix by screwing or nailing (a perforated galvanised strap to secure components together, before doing other works is a sensible precaution)
- look for any old repairs that were intended to 'cure' the problem but have in fact only deferred it(!) – for example, purlins or hip boards propped on ceiling joists and which will eventually start to bend themselves under the load, which has only been temporarily redistributed but not properly supported)
- check the condition of any adjacent roof
- check the weight of the new covering, if a replacement is intended (all too often, replacement concrete tiles are found to have overloaded an old roof, with no reinforcement works to the old timber frame to accommodate them)
- when re-roofing (i.e. a new covering, rather than repairs to the old), check that the valleys are left 'open' (rather than closed by overhanging tile edges) to ensure any leaf blockages or mould deposits can be raked out quite easily.

It is often the case that, unless you observe any very significant shortcomings and the roof is currently performing adequately, it might be best to leave well alone, although a cautionary comment to the Building Owner may be appropriate to advise that eventually an improvement or repair might be required.

If you are appointed by the client in the role of Clerk of Works, you will also get some idea of the quality of site workmanship and the need for early intervention by observing the following:

- **Stacking of slates or tiles on the roof before they are laid** – It is particularly important to ensure that the load is distributed evenly over the roof rather than stacked up in one corner, which can completely overload either the battens or possibly even the rafters beneath. (Poor stacking will also give you an early warning of worse to come if you are not quick to check the progress!)
- **The quality of work from felt upwards** – For example, the felt needs to be sufficiently loose to allow water to drain beneath the battens; and if it is a traditional roof, any timber battens should be stopped off 200 mm (about 8 inches) from flues to reduce fire risk.
- **Are properly tanalised/chemically treated timber battens being used to resist timber decay?** – Counter-battening may be appropriate in particularly exposed positions.
- **Is the gauge suitable?** – Less scrupulous roofing contractors and builders may be inclined to 'pull the gauge' in order to reduce the number of rows of tiles used and slightly reduce costs. The effect of this, of course, is that there is insufficient lap on the tiles and much increased risk of driven water penetration.

The box, Roofs – the basics, should serve as a useful aide memoire when you are out on a site inspection.

Tiles stacked on roofs to spread the load.

ROOFS – THE BASICS

Traditional 'cut timber' roofs

These are simple frames, as sketched below, which are likely to include purlins and probably some props or struts to support the purlins and relieve some load onto internal walls (hopefully load-bearing, but not always).

In practice, the loads imposed by the roof covering (the dead loads) and the live loads, such as wind, rain, snow and occasional builders and their ladders, are transmitted in a pattern: the feet or lower ends of the rafters will tend to want to push outwards; the top of the rafters will want to push together as the feet push out.

So, in checking works on an old or new structure it is important to establish that the timbers on each side of the roof are suitably opposed and that the loads cancel each other out by pushing against each other more or less equally on each side of the ridge board.

The purlin should be fixed at about, or just below, the halfway point up the roof slope. That way, it not only picks up some of the weight and loading from the rafters, it also helps restrain the outward thrust tendencies of the rafters. If the purlin is above the halfway point, it will be in the area where the rafters are pushing together, and will not be in a position to offer any restraint.

Simple; or at least it should be. Experience suggests, however, that this straightforward and desirable state of affairs is not so often found in practice!

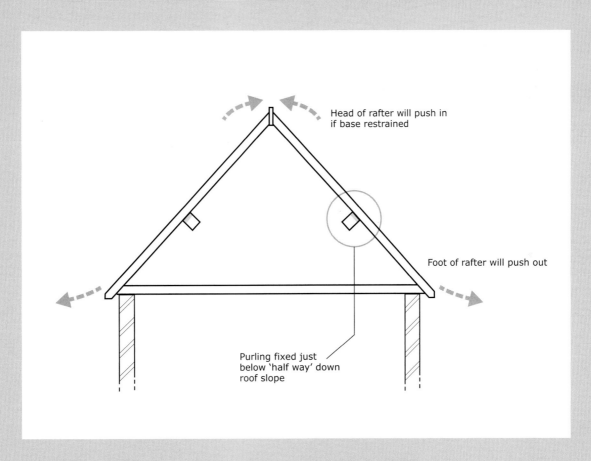

Head of rafter will push in if base restrained

Foot of rafter will push out

Purling fixed just below 'half way' down roof slope

Pre-trussed roofs

The timber pre-trussed rafter frame has been the dominant roof construction since the late 1960s (see illustration overleaf).

The frames are comparatively quick and simple to erect in most situations and can be pre-designed for specific load or span factors and then manufactured off-site, reducing reliance on skilled onsite labour and fair weather (though erecting the frames in high winds is not desirable for obvious reasons).

Single pitched roofs

Typically, this type of roof is found on single-storey additions for, say, a kitchen or outhouse in an old terraced house. Often prone to particular problems caused by the difficulty of tying-in the frame. Over time, single pitch roofs can sag or collapse quite badly.

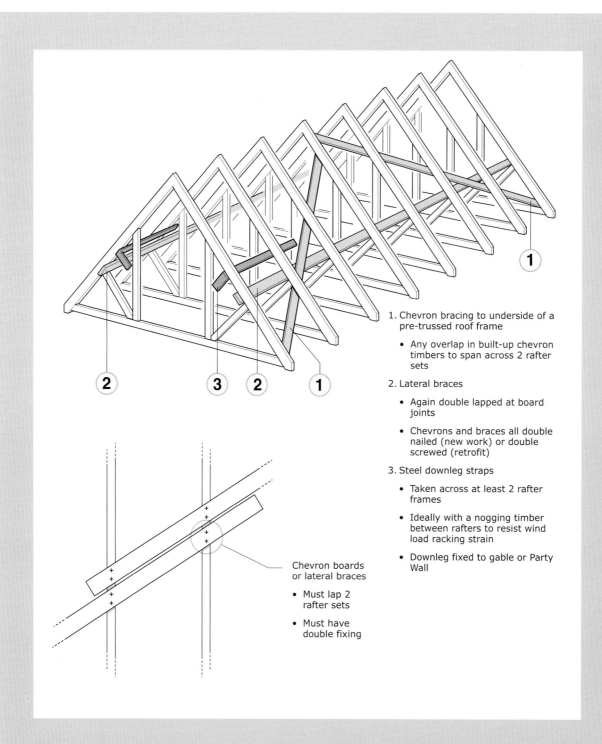

1. Chevron bracing to underside of a pre-trussed roof frame

   • Any overlap in built-up chevron timbers to span across 2 rafter sets

2. Lateral braces

   • Again double lapped at board joints

   • Chevrons and braces all double nailed (new work) or double screwed (retrofit)

3. Steel downleg straps

   • Taken across at least 2 rafter frames

   • Ideally with a nogging timber between rafters to resist wind load racking strain

   • Downleg fixed to gable or Party Wall

Chevron boards or lateral braces

   • Must lap 2 rafter sets

   • Must have double fixing

PITCHED ROOF COVERINGS

Slate

Once perhaps the most common covering of pitched roofs, slate has fallen into something of a decline in favour of the ubiquitous concrete tile. But it still has much to recommend it despite being (usually) a more expensive option than the concrete version.

You should not neglect the aesthetics of re-roofing a period property with its original style of covering (assuming of course it was slate) though it can be hard to persuade the Building Owner of the merits of using a more expensive material.

Slate is generally a much lighter covering than concrete tiles. This means that it is often possible to avoid roof frame repairs and reinforcement when re-roofing in slate (although in all instances of re-roofing work it is important to check the integrity of the frame and fixings prior to any work).

If you do specify repairs to a slate roof, remember that it may be possible to re-use some of the slates by turning them round. And if re-covering in a different material, check that any value in the old slate stock is set off against the cost of the works. (Be wary of the contractor's '98% breakages' – if fairly sound slates are removed, the slate itself might not be significantly affected by wear and tear (in the case of nail sickness, for example). The breakages have a nasty habit of being carefully stacked out of sight and may never make it as far as the skip.)

The typical slate size is the 'two-by-one', that is to say, 2 ft × 1 ft in old money (600 mm × 300 mm), and

the best quality slate, and by far the most expensive, is the Welsh Blue.

Slates come in difference thicknesses too, which also affects the price, the weight and the expected lifespan of the covering. The better quality slate will be more impervious to frost, and is likely to offer much better value in the long run.

Consider the wearing qualities carefully before making any recommendations to the client. Study the supplier's brochure carefully; and a reliable and experienced roofer can probably offer some advice as well.

Slate roofs – hip details

- Usually follow the cheapest option! Covered in ridge/hip tiles with lowest hip slate secured by a 'hip iron' bracket screwed into the hip board

- But in better class work could be a

Mitred slate hip over a sheet lead soaker beneath (min code 4 lead) or one of the following:

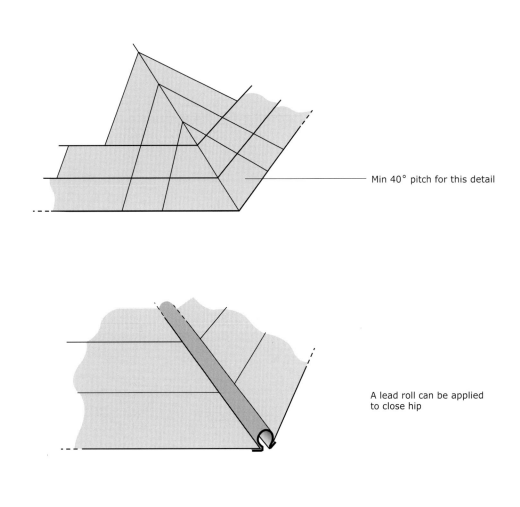

Min 40° pitch for this detail

A lead roll can be applied to close hip

Where the roof meets a gable or parapet abutment – usually detailed as a soaker and cover flashing

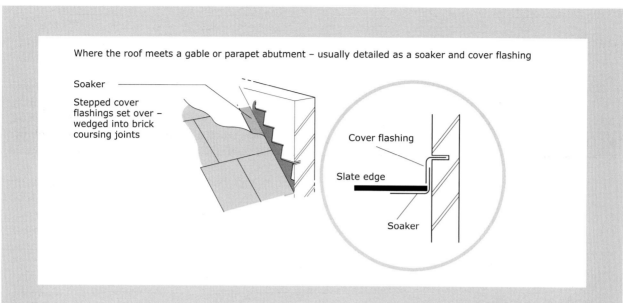

Soaker

Stepped cover flashings set over – wedged into brick coursing joints

Cover flashing

Slate edge

Soaker

Slate roof detailing

- Slates normally have double lap (can be as little as 1/3 at sides)
- Laid to BS 5534 and . . .
- To BS 8104 driving rain index – governs the lap needed to prevent driven pain penetration

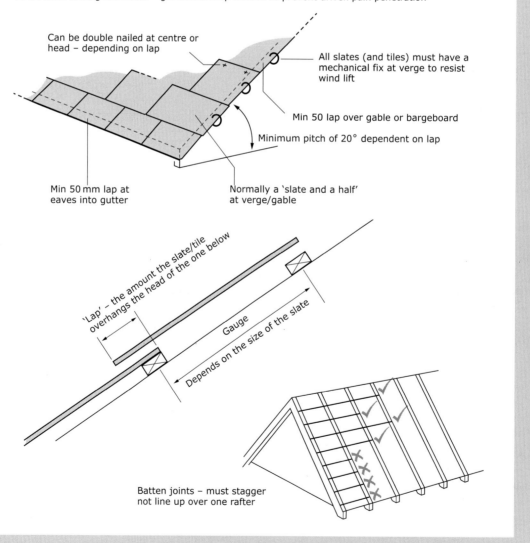

Can be double nailed at centre or head – depending on lap

All slates (and tiles) must have a mechanical fix at verge to resist wind lift

Min 50 lap over gable or bargeboard

Minimum pitch of 20° dependent on lap

Min 50 mm lap at eaves into gutter

Normally a 'slate and a half' at verge/gable

'Lap' – the amount the slate/tile overhangs the head of the one below

Gauge

Depends on the size of the slate

Batten joints – must stagger not line up over one rafter

Alternatives to slate

Alternatives to natural slate include:

- **Asbestos cement slate** – Less often encountered now, these generally had a lifespan of about 40 years. As the slates aged they were prone to curl up at the edges, resembling a dried out sandwich.
- **The Eternit™ and other fibre–cement slate composites** – These normally require a copper rivet and washer to be fixed through a hole at the bottom of the slate to resist wind lift, which may otherwise snap the slate. The fibre–cement composite slate does not have a laminated structure in the same way as a natural slate and is comparatively weak. Consequently, this type of product may not be best suited to an aggressive weather aspect (buildings on a seafront spring to mind).
- **Pressed slate composites** – Made of resin and slate dust (fairly realistic).

Many of the problems associated with synthetic slates (particularly curling at the edges and sometimes bowing or bending, and general lack of flatness) are generally attributed to a moisture build-up under the slate. With roofing felts being obligatory, there is likely to be much less through-flow of air under the slate; consequently, this issue may continue for the foreseeable future.

If this is an issue, you might consider counter-battening the roof in order to create more of an air space beneath, i.e. lining battens over the rafters and then applying the main roofing battens along the line of the roof in the traditional way. This may reduce the problem to some extent, but of course this is an additional cost that is likely to be resisted, except on the most expensive schemes where composite slates are unlikely to be used anyway!

Slate alternatives do, however, offer a solution where weight needs to be limited, and where cost is an issue, or where the use of a concrete tile is to be avoided for cosmetic or other reasons.

Concrete tiles

Concrete tiles are probably the most commonly used roof covering material of the last 30 years or so, mainly due to the lower cost. But the tiles do weigh considerably more than a slate covering, so the roof frame has to be strong to bear this weight.

When re-roofing using concrete tiles, it is essential to check that any additional bracing timbers, new purlins and struts, for example, have been installed properly first.

Concrete tiles are prone to their own particular problems – usually those associated with concrete products in general, i.e. attack from chlorides and acid.

A marine climate or exposed position could lead to wind-driven sea salt contamination and thus to chloride attack; while areas prone to acid rainfall might also suffer from problems because of the dissolving of the top layer of the tile and rapid washing out of the fine aggregate material from the top.

This might not initially affect the performance of the tile itself, but large amounts of aggregate (loosened as the cement binder is dissolved by the acid rain) washing into the gutters, downpipes and (particularly) soak away chambers can lead to a quick deterioration in the efficiency of the surface water drainage system. Re-calcified fines from the tiles are extremely difficult to shift from blocked underground drain systems, especially in clayware land drain pipes, which may have to be total replaced.

The worst case I have seen involved concrete tiles dating from about 1930, which were very spongy, having deteriorated quite significantly. This was on a development of bungalows situated on a hillside in Lancing, built between the First and Second World Wars.

Concrete tiles do offer a great range of design, shape, size and weight, and can generally be produced to emulate any of the styles of clay tile. So, although the tiles with interlocking edges are perhaps the most common, nevertheless a range of coloured and sized plain tiles (i.e. flat ones) is available, providing various options to help fit in with prevailing local architectural details.

Clay tiles

Most people would probably agree that clay tiles offer a significant aesthetic advantage over concrete tiles but usually at some increased cost.

The clay tile, in particular, can be prone to frost damage, and if you are specifying a tile this should always be considered, especially where cheaper tiles are involved. It is possible that tiles imported from warmer climes may not achieve the performance standard needed in the UK.

Where concrete or clay tiles are used in an exposed area prone to high wind loads they can be prone to chatter as the wind ripples through the lower lapped edges of the tiles. Double lapping the tiles may reduce this tendency to some extent, but in very exposed areas it is possible (and advisable) to clip the lower edge of the tiles in a similar fashion to the composite slates described above.

Clay tiles (and clay bricks too) can be prone to effluorescence. (See Chapter 9; Problem 9.11.)

Novel products

Various forms of photovoltaic slate are coming to the market, and although you will probably not be called upon for repairs-related advice in the near future, you may find clients asking about these products when re-roofing or major renovations are being considered. You will need to establish whether insurers are happy to cover the risks; I have experienced problems on commercial projects due to insurers' concerns about electrical arcing at conductor connections, and with earthing.

For social housing schemes, in particular, roof covering materials must be selected to demonstrate a sustainable approach. Where in the past concrete tiles have been popular because of their low cost and comparatively low environmental rating (EcoHomes), other options are becoming available – ranging from tiles made from recycled materials such as tyres to 'green roofs' planted with sedum – though each will have a range of benefits and drawbacks.

FLAT ROOFS AND COVERINGS

Flat roofs, beloved of the housing booms of the '60s and '70s, are fraught with problems due to design, materials and workmanship, and they rarely have an extended lifespan when compared with a pitched roof.

The majority of flat roofs are covered in a roofing felt – usually one of the cheaper felts at that. The flat roofing industry has also been plagued by contractors carrying out shoddy work which undermines the performance that could be achieved by properly detailed flat roof coverings.

A typical cheaper domestic roofing felt (we are not talking shed grade felt here … at least we shouldn't be) with a fibreglass mat base will last 10 or perhaps 15 years. A synthetic membrane may last longer depending on its situation, the quality of the workmanship and so on. It will, of course, be rather more expensive.

Well-constructed mastic asphalt coverings on flat roofs can perform very well and are one of the options to consider for roof gardens, for example, where turf is overlaid. However, it will probably cost more than most felt systems. There are also modern roofing membranes designed to accommodate this type of detail.

So, it is easy to see that we are in a position where a large number of roofs in the nation's housing stock will be failing or about to fail at any given time. Rather than simply replacing or recovering them like-for-like you then have the opportunity to make some improvements. Options include:

a. Improve the roof fall and reduce water ponding up on the roof. (Many flat roofs have a completely inadequate amount of fall and do not shed water properly, causing differential thermal movement patterns, stressing the covering and accelerating failures.)
b. Improve the lifespan and type of covering material.
c. Improve the roof insulation possibly in conjunction with (a) above.

I would suggest you always:

- advise the client about the risks inherent with flat roofs and their generally limited life expectancy
- consider the quality of any guarantees offered by contractors, what surety they can offer, and whether there are special terms (some manufacturers only warrant the product if it has been inspected by one of their representatives)
- check that the workmanship comes with a guarantee over and above the guarantee for the material
- remember to record your advice to the client in writing (the budget will frequently control the specification choice, so your advice may not always be adopted).

Roofing felt

Roofing felt is the most common covering. It is usually the cheapest solution and is found on thousands or even millions of domestic and commercial smaller buildings throughout the UK.

Before effecting a repair you need to carefully consider the reasons for failure. Obviously the most common and straightforward is the felt perishing once it has reached the end of its life (at ten years or so). Look carefully at the various specifications and grades of felt before advising your client.

Mastic asphalt

Mastic asphalt is a blend of rock asphalt and bitumen. Detailing standards are set out in BS 6925. In *Building Elements: Roofs and Roofing: Performance, diagnosis, maintenance, repair and the avoidance of defects* (BRE, 2000; ISBN: 978 1 86081 068 3), HW Harrison suggests an achievable lifespan of up to 60 years if well-maintained, and indeed the asphalt-covered flat roof and roof garden covering the former staff flats built for Cunard in the heart of Southampton lasted some 60 years or so before needing any attention.

Lead and copper

Sheet lead also offers potential high performance as a roof covering, and it may be a mandatory requirement to use it on a Listed Building or in a conservation area.

It is, of course, heavy – especially when used in the heavier/thicker gauges, which may be needed for exposed situations. And it is expensive – not just for the material.

This is not a material/finish to leave to chance. If you need to prepare a specification then I would urge you to read *Rolled Lead Sheet – The Complete Manual* (June 2007) published by the Lead Sheet Association (*www.leadsheetassociation.org.uk*). This book replaces the old three-volume version, and although it is not cheap it offers very sound advice with numerous diagrams, enabling you to specify with confidence in a variety of situations.

If setting up very simple jobs, data sheets from the manufacturer are also likely to be helpful, and simple lead detailing should be within the capacity of most building firms. However, although many builders and roofers 'do' lead work there are comparatively few firms that can address the more complicated and detailed jobs with confidence.

The first port of call in these situations may be to approach your local Cathedral Works Organisation (a quick search on the Internet should find one close to your project), or the local authority's conservation officers to see which firms are active and competent in the local area.

Poor attention to detailing and the use of the wrong lead gauge have led to huge numbers of unnecessary failures and water penetration problems. Even comparatively minor omissions can sometimes direct significant amounts of water to places it should not go (i.e. indoors, and often visible dripping down a light pendant or onto an electrical switch).

When supervising works it is important to check detail items such as:

- whether the ends of any damp-proof trays are turned the right way and not full of mortar slovens and drips, and that the weeps are not blocked
- whether the lengths of lead are short enough to allow for any thermal movement and prevent fissuring and cracking to the lead (which can occur quite quickly, if not).

Copper is much less used on flat roofs than all the other sheet materials; the techniques are broadly similar to lead work (for example, traditional joints can normally be formed in a 'roll' both in lead work or sheet copper).

Considering the appropriate tolerances for gauge, thermal movement, exposure, and climate is essential, and again a suitably competent and experienced contractor needs to be selected.

Copper can be formed as a standing seam where the edges of the copper sheet are turned up and a section of copper strip folded over to close the seam and make it watertight. This system is often employed on sheet aluminium roofing as well. Standing seams are generally only employed on pitches over about 60 degrees; below that, it would be usual to use a traditional wooden roll technique to form the laps of the sheet material.

Milled sheet lead needs to be of an appropriate gauge for the level of exposure and spans of the sheet lead to be used, and where sheet copper is used it needs to be annealed to British Standard 2870, which advises various grades within the standard.

Sheet metal materials can generally be nailed or use 'boss' fixings which are capped over with some similar metal sweated in place to seal the fixing.

Care needs to be taken to prevent galvanic corrosion occurring, i.e. using two different metals with different electrical potential means that corrosion begins because the different electrolytic potentials of the two materials interact to form a conductor as soon as it rains.

When fixing copper, for example, nail fixings should be of copper or copper alloy. Screws need to be brass. Steel screws might be used to fix lead rolls, but if there is the slightest possibility of other metals coming into contact it would be better not to use them. A minimum measure would certainly be to countersink screw fixings to ensure none of the metal fixings touch the covering.

With both sheet copper and sheet lead it would be usual to employ a felt underlay. This provides a slip-plane to prevent thermal stressed movement affecting the decking and substrate and, in the case of copper, it would also provide an electrical insulation layer to prevent the covering touching any steel fixing nails. It also tends to reduce wind and rain noise.

Special fixing techniques are generally required where low-density roof decks are used (e.g. wood–wool slab) although this is less commonly used in modern construction than perhaps 30 years ago.

A particular advantage of a copper roof is that it can be combined to form part of the lightning conductor system for a building, although the values would require careful calculation (British Standard Code of Practice 326), and suitable detailing is necessary to resist the risk of galvanic corrosion where other materials may well be combined.

Sheet metal coverings weather differently. Lead tends to provide a consistent pale grey colour, but it is important to ensure a suitable patination oil is used – without it, green staining can result (particularly where the sheet lead is in contact with cement mortar), and this tends to look somewhat unsightly and patchy.

Copper roofs are well known for their green, weathered colour, which is a natural process and a feature of this material – but it would be well worth emphasising this aspect to Clients, who may not fully appreciate the potential of the copper sheet to weather down in this way.

Aluminium sheet covered roofs are unlikely to weather significantly, apart from the surface of the material matting down and losing its shine, and is likely to present a very clean finish suitable for modern building styles.

At the time of writing, the Federation of Traditional Metal Roofing Contractors (FTMRC) is preparing a Good Practice Manual for sheet metals (excluding lead). (See *www.ftmrc.co.uk*.)

Asbestos cement and fibre cement profiled sheets

This type of covering material has been used in vast quantities, particularly on speculatively built industrial and warehousing developments. The material was the mainstay of many developments from about the 1930s through to the '50s and '60s.

Although asbestos cement sheeting has many advantages – including the cheapness, and ease of fixing and cutting – nevertheless, the vast acreages of estates built using this material are now likely to be nearing the end of their lifespan, if they have not been replaced already.

Health and safety risks are associated with asbestos contained in old roofing sheets, but there are other issues affecting the specification of replacements if a like-for-like modern fibre cement sheet is not to be used. You will need to check the weight of the sheeting. Will it need regular maintenance (and therefore access)? Are safety harness fixings required? Is the roof sub-frame strong enough?

PCM sheet roofs

Plastic-coated metal (PCM) sheet roofing came into significant use during the late 1970s. Typically, this is based on a profiled steel sheet, but other materials are also in use – aluminium probably being the most common.

The plastic coating on a sheet metal covering typically lasts 10–15 years before it starts to flake away, and regular maintenance is normally required to maintain the condition of the material.

You will often find that the manufacturer's warranty is based on (indeed stipulates) annual maintenance, which therefore somewhat dilutes the impact of using a cheap covering.

PROBLEMS – ROOFS AND RAINWATER GOODS

10.1 MOSS AND LICHEN

Both clay and concrete tiled roofs are prone to a build up of moss or lichens – particularly concrete tiles which have a rough aggregate surface where fine material is bonded onto the surface of the tile, which provides an idea anchor for moss growth.

A significant build up of moss can increase the weight of the tile by holding a large amount of water; a moderate build up of moss is unlikely to significantly affect any loading values onto the roof.

Solution

If the growth of moss or lichen is a problem it can be addressed with chemical treatment, but this requires significant health and safety precautions to dispose of any run-off and to prevent contamination to flora and fauna within the garden or soak aways.

Lightning-quick way to prevent moss
An effective way to prevent this problem is to bond strips of copper wire across the roof surface. As it becomes wetted down by the weather the copper provides a copper salt wash over the roof surface, providing a low level toxic herbicide to prevent moss growth obtaining a foothold. (I have found that strips of thin lightning conductor material strapped along the ridgeline are reasonably effective.)

Although remarkably straightforward, clients seem generally quite reluctant to adopt this measure.

10.2 WIND-INDUCED DISTORTION OF PRE-TRUSSED ROOFS

The original specification for these pre-trussed roofs (sometimes known as 'TRADA roofs') was subsequently amended to include lateral and chevron or diagonal bracing timbers to reinforce the roof across its width, mainly to take account of the loads imposed, probably onto one aspect of the roof only, by the prevailing wind.

Many pre-trussed roofs have now been improved by retro-fitting bracing timbers and steel strap anchors. But equally many have not, and large numbers are still encountered needing some works, if only as a precautionary measure.

Properties in sheltered locations may be at comparatively low risk from distortion of the frame due to wind loads, nevertheless it is only sensible to recommend repairs in accordance with the BRE Good Building Guides 8 and 16 (see *www.brebookshop.com*).

Solution 1

Timber diagonal bracing boards should be fixed to the underside of the rafter frames, with each fixing secured beneath the rafter at two points. The diagonal spars are often made up of two or more sections overlapped, depending on the height of the roof. Overlaps need to cross over at least two rafter sets to achieve adequate load spread.

The fixings could be nailed, but I would recommend screw fixings – certainly in any situation where a retro-fit is being handled – because it is amazing how much damage vibration can cause to plaster finishes (especially thin coats of plaster skimmed over nail heads or plasterboard joints).

Solution 2

Likewise in any retro-fit situation it is likely that the chevron braces will have to be built up in several sections unless you are particularly lucky in finding a roof access trap hatch and landing area large enough to manhandle the lengths of timber required!

Before fixing extra restraining timbers in place it is well worth while checking for any distortion in the pre-trussed frames.

The handbook Building Elements: *Roofs and Roofing: Performance, diagnosis, maintenance, repair and the avoidance of defects* (2000; ISBN: 978 1 86081 068 8) advises that lateral distortions in the frame out of true by 10 mm in 1 m of rise are probably capable of being rectified. If the lateral distortion is greater than 40 mm overall, you should have the frames checked by a Chartered Structural Engineer to consider their structural integrity before proceeding further (probable candidates for replacement?).

Rafter frame and wall collapse in Normandy.

10.3 STABILISING A NEW PRE-TRUSSED ROOF

New buildings with pre-trussed frames should incorporate perforated galvanised steel down leg straps to secure the wall plate and help resist plate rotating, and prevent wind suction exerting excess pull on it. This is an area where it is difficult to effect a repair unless the Building Owner is prepared to accept plaster being chased out within the top floor to fix the straps to the inner face of the wall (always assuming a masonry wall of course).

When carrying out new work, ensure that the straps are actually fixed – often they are there, but not secured.

Solution

Down leg straps can easily be fixed onto the gable wall, and across the two frame assemblies, in each end of a conventionally gabled roof in accordance with the installation recommendations (as illustrated opposite). This provides a degree of improvement, but a fully specified wall plate strap down has to be optimal.

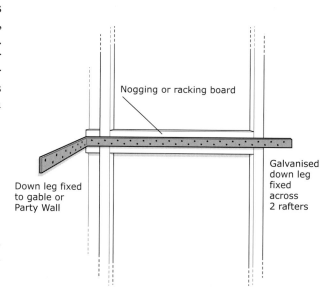

Nogging or racking board

Down leg fixed to gable or Party Wall

Galvanised down leg fixed across 2 rafters

Rafters viewed from beneath.

COST SEQUENCE – Retro-fitting bracing to pre-trussed roofs

1. Cut rough timber 100 mm by 12.5 mm section nominal into sufficient lengths to pass into the roof space. Allow for battening to the underside of rafters.
2. Double screw all fixing positions on chevron 'V'. Ensure that any overlaps between boards are taken across a minimum of 2 rafter sets.
3. Run horizontal/lateral braces across the underside of rafters or internal chord positions. Again allow for doubling up fixings across rafter positions/over laps to make up board lengths. Double screw all fixings to roof timbers.
4. Ensure that lateral braces (one for each roof slope) terminate within 10 mm or less of internal face of gable

walls to take up any racking and prevent slack within the braces.
5. Fix galvanised 38 mm by 4 mm section steel down leg straps passed across minimum 2 rafter sets at each gable end. Screw fix to underside face of rafters and allow for minimum of 2 screw fixings plugged to internal face of gable wall. Allow for 1 down leg fixing per roof slope/gable wall abutment.
6. Pricing assumes a typical roof plan section size of 7 m in each direction and typical roof pitch of 35 degrees.

Retro-fitting bracing to pre-trussed roofs – COST £900

10.4 TRUSSED RAFTERS AND HOME IMPROVEMENTS

A quite surprising number of Building Owners seem unable to resist the urge to 'go into' the roof space for storage or to create a hobbies' or computer room (no longer is the roof space the realm of the Hornby train set!).

The first things to go are the 'excessively inconvenient' struts, spars and chords, which are sawn away at a whim. This never ceases to amaze me; what did the householder think the timbers were there for in the first place?

These improvements (usually) quickly become apparent from the outside – the clearly visible sagging of the external surface of the roof. The edges of interlocking tiles often become unlocked in the process because the slight curvature of the roof causes the roofing battens to bend and the tiles to kick up out of line. The ceiling joists may also start to sag, causing joints between plasterboard sheets to open and the plaster over the nail heads to pop off in the ceiling, if the ceiling bends under the now-unrestrained loads of the new floor or the pre-existing water tank.

If the roof is over a block of timber-framed flats, then the situation can only get worse because of the various ownerships and interests involved in the resolution. Nevertheless, you should seriously consider a new roof frame. For example, if considerable repairs are required (which is likely) it may be very difficult to establish load-bearing walls on which to temporarily support the structure, in addition to the disruption to the other residents which may result if temporary support needs to be taken up through each floor of the building.

Solution

If distortions prove minimal, it is possible to reinstate the framework by inserting new struts with oversized plywebs to plate over the new connecting points. Such a repair is suitable for all dwelling types, but a few extra investigations are needed before proceeding (particularly for flats, given all the various 'interests' involved):

- Careful consideration of legal as well as structural issues is required in this situation; do other residents need temporary relocation and so on?
- Is an insurance backed claim from other residents against the defaulting flat owner likely?
- Will it hinder the repairs process? Will this property (and the others) be mortgage-worthy if the works are done in a particular way?
- Should the works be supervised by a Chartered Building Surveyor or a Chartered Structural Engineer? (Some mortgage lenders are surprisingly choosy about using one, or the other!)

10.5 TRADITIONAL ROOFS: UNSECURED POLING BOARD

Older roofs (pre-Second World War typically) may use a poling board detail. This seems to be a regional favourite; it is certainly common on the south coast.

The rafters are fixed to the poling board, which can sometimes slide on the rafters (any fixings, if there were any, having parted company long ago).

A telltale sign of an advanced problem is bulging of the fascia board or heavily gapped soffits at the face of the wall suggesting the rafters are now starting to nudge their way outwards.

Solution

Poling boards can normally be secured with screws skewed in at an angle, or with a galvanised mild steel strap lapped over the board and screwed to both the ceiling joists and the poling board (and sometimes also to the rafters).

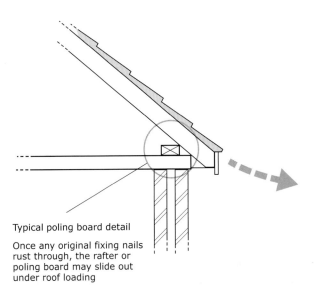

Typical poling board detail

Once any original fixing nails rust through, the rafter or poling board may slide out under roof loading

10.6 INADEQUATE PURLIN END BEARINGS

The size and fixing of the original purlins can be something of a hit and miss affair, so check the position and section sizes of the purlin (for example, against the TRADA loading tables: *Span tables for solid timber members in floors, ceilings and roofs for dwellings*; ISBN 978 1 900510 46 4).

Ideally, when installing new purlins and props, the props should be angled at about 90 degrees to the line of the roof surface to obtain maximum efficiency from the prop, and reduce the likelihood of it bending or being pushed by a lateral load.

Frequently they cling onto the gable or Party Wall by the equivalent of their fingernails. Often any old soft red brick providing support may have now compressed and crumbled away (wartime bomb damage may have taken its toll too). Remember – cheap bricks were often used on the hidden parts of older buildings (not always just older ones either) and the brick stock may well be badly under-fired and consequently the brick could be quite soft.

- Don't assume that because the front elevation looks all right then everything else is as well. Facing bricks were frequently reserved only for the front elevation, especially in cheaper housing stock.
- Establish that the props or struts supporting the purlin locate onto something useful (such as a load-bearing wall). All too frequently there was no wall within reach of the convenient bit of timber the builder had to hand, and the prop might be found to cantilever onto a ceiling joist.
- Ensure that the wall is continuous and offers full support down to foundation level. Just because the bit at the top under load looks solid doesn't mean that it really is!

The case of the sagging first floor

A common problem in an area where I worked for many years was the 'improvement' of small flat-fronted mid-terraced houses, which had serious consequences for the continuity of load support. For example, the separating wall between the lounge and dining room would have been removed, often leaving minimal (if any) piers, sometimes with only perfunctory support to the first floor spine wall – which in turn picked up the roof load from the purlin props and sometimes part of the first floor too!

I was often called in to advise a perplexed householder who had purchased a lovely 'builder modernised' project, where they couldn't account for the sagging first floor that had developed, or perhaps the tears through the woodchip wallpaper lining.

Luckily, conveyancing lawyers are now much more alive to the risks of previous alterations and the pre-contract enquiries aim to address this.

The introduction of the HIP reports may raise awareness of the risks and costs involved in rectifying substandard or poorly considered works; and consequently there will be an ongoing need for repair works to badly modernised housing stock.

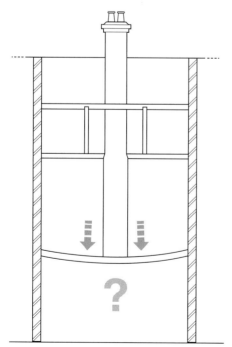

Load-bearing wall removed as part of 'improvements'.

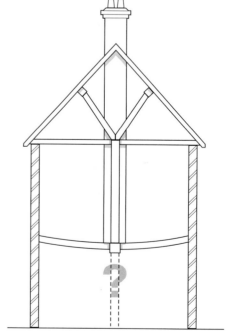

Load from purlin props, chimney and floor may all impact on the 'missing' wall.

Solution 1

If the purlin sits upright in section then a conventional joist hanger may be used to pick up the end and provide an adequate fixing to the wall.

Alternatively, a steel angle 'shelf' fixed to the wall may also provide a good bearing, with the angle fixed to the wall using lengths of stud bolt glued into sockets in the brick using a polyester resin to provide a very strong bond (provided the bricks are not too fragile). (See diagram below).

Otherwise it may be appropriate to carefully have part of the brick course chased out and a reinforced concrete lintel let in to provide a suitably dense bearing (shown below).

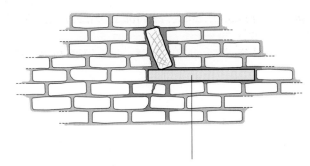

Reinforced concrete (RC) lintel let in to soft brick to support purlin end and prevent continued fracturing to soft brick support

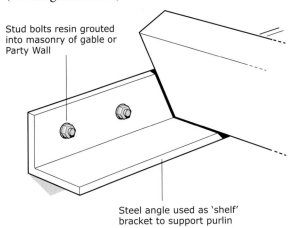

Stud bolts resin grouted into masonry of gable or Party Wall

Steel angle used as 'shelf' bracket to support purlin

- Timber blocks may be required to 'locate' the purlin and prevent it sliding on the shelf
- Assess the masonry. Are the bricks sufficiently robust? Is a longer shelf or more bolts needed to spread the load?

Bear in mind that if the wall is a party structure you will need to serve a Party Wall Act Notice if the fabric or loading is being modified in any way.

You should also ensure that the purlin has adequate fire protection on a Party Wall.

COST SEQUENCE – Improve purlin end bearings

Improve fixity to purlin end bearings and installation of single purlin prop on each of 2 roof slope elevations (traditional cut roof).

1. Fix steel angle shelf beneath each purlin end bearing. Allow for minimum angle shelf with nominal 100 mm faces. Allow for minimum 3 no. M15 stud bolt fixings resin grouted into drilled sockets in masonry to inner leaf of gable wall. Use folding wedges to tighten end bearing to purlin as required.
2. Locate position close to centre of purlin span and cut purlin prop, in minimum 100 mm by 50 mm section soft wood to locate on internal load bearing wall.

3. Fix timber plate to head of internal wall to receive props.
4. Oppose props onto timber plate and secure with timber gusset/web with screw fixings to side faces of purlin props. Allow for 2 gussets – one to each side of the props.
5. Allow for folding wedges to tighten fixing/bearing points of prop to underside of purlin.

NB: No allowance made for any Party Wall Act service, which may be required for Party Walls receiving purlin end bearings.

Improve purlin end bearings and install purlin props – COST £380

10.7 OTHER PURLIN PROBLEMS

If the purlin is at its most efficient position (just under the halfway point of the roof slope) then the purlin props may not conveniently secure onto a central load-bearing wall within the property at the right angle. Obviously it all depends on the size and angle of the roof.

Solution 1

Within limits, a departure from the ideal right angle of prop to roof pitch line may be acceptable. But, if the angle is too severe you may need to consider some other options.

Using two (or more) purlins per slope to avoid the need for any (or many) props is one possibility.

Solution 2

Another possibility is to oppose the ends of the purlin props onto a stiff beam (probably timber), which is in turn secured onto a load-bearing wall accessible from within the roof void.

This is feasible provided the loads on each side of the beam would be fairly equal and the beam can be secured and there is no risk of it seesawing or tipping over. It will probably be necessary to secure the bottom of the props onto the beam to prevent this.

Solution 3

The use of galvanised perforated mild steel strap or perhaps of plywood webs is useful.

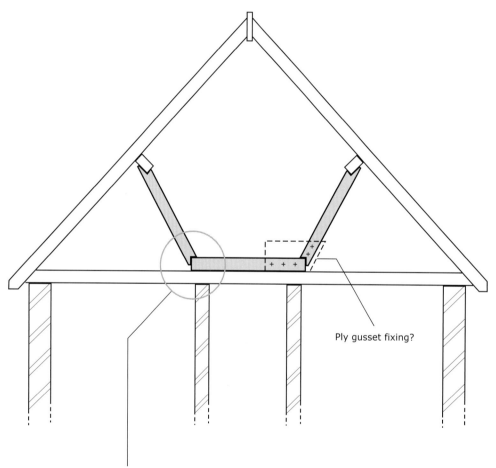

Ply gusset fixing?

Approximately equal purlin loads are taken by props onto, e.g., a substantial timber beam supported in turn on load bearing walls. Typically enclosing walls around the staircase in a terraced house

The joints between the props and bearer could be reinforced with a ply gusset screw-fixed over

Plywood web fixings or plates – typically using a reasonable quality of 12 mm (minimum) plywood to secure together timber joints – is a very sound way of locking together timber by creating a sandwich, providing the elements are of uniform thickness. (Any new timbers inserted as the 'jam' in the sandwich need to match the existing ones to prevent distortion or weaknesses being created).

It is worth ensuring that any critical fixing points are secured using a good quality shear resistant screw – preferably one with a known rated shear strength, particularly where any calculations are required. This emulates the style of gang nail plate fixings found in trussed rafters or joists and provides a very solid fix, while spreading the fixing stresses across a wider area than a simple nailed or screwed joint.

Solution 4

Using plywood webs (see above) can assist with supporting a failing roof onto a new load-bearing ridge beam. For example, if the rafters are not properly opposed and an old ridge board has started to buckle and fail, then a series of new ply roof apex webs can be formed to hang the ridge onto a new timber (or steel) load-bearing ridge beam, which in turn can be supported onto props onto the load-bearing walls.

Checks:

● Have the load capacities of the web, screw fixings and supporting posts checked before proceeding, and ensure that Building Control is comfortable with this solution.

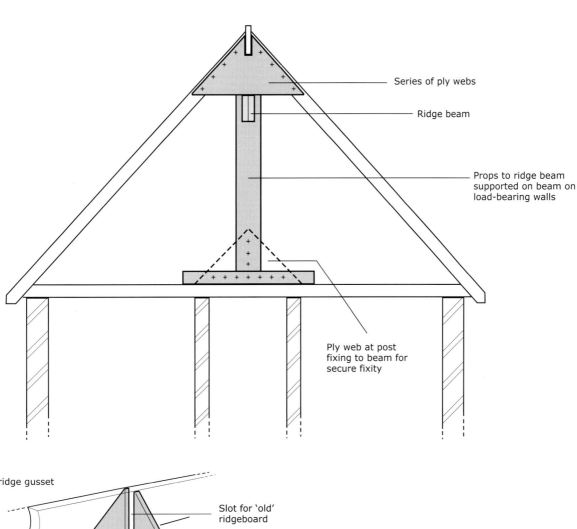

Series of ply webs

Ridge beam

Props to ridge beam supported on beam on load-bearing walls

Ply web at post fixing to beam for secure fixity

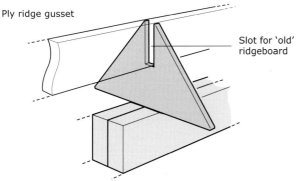

Ply ridge gusset

Slot for 'old' ridgeboard

- Sometimes the load path and foundations need to be checked and the footing reinforced – perhaps by simple and localised concrete underpinning of the load-bearing wall to pick up the new load transfer. Establish this before specifying and getting the works quoted; or explain the risks in terms of cost and delay (engineer and Building Control) if the client wants to chance it. The risk is theirs, but you need to make it very clear that this may be required as the works progress.

COST SEQUENCE – Plywood web repair to top of rafters/bending ridge board

1. Cut triangular ply webs to fit apex/roof pitch. Cut slot through apex of web to accommodate the ridge beam/ridge board. Use minimum 25 mm plywood.
2. Fix web to one face of rafters slotted over the existing ridge board. Allow for minimum 5 screw fixings per rafter slope in premium quality screws rated for shear resistance or use, say, M10 engineering stud bolt.
3. Fix ply gusset/web to each rafter set.
4. Locate new ridge beam beneath the plywood bearings formed in the apex. Allow for folding wedges to finally tension once fixed.
5. Timber ridge beam assumed of nominal section 200 mm by 50 mm to be located onto timber prop's

minimum section size 100 mm by 50 mm taken to load bearing walls internally.
6. Allow for 20 no. engineering stud bolts to be resin grout socketed to adjoining walls with PVC damp-proof course sleeved beneath to isolate any timber from potentially exposed wall surfaces.
7. Allow for stripping back the roof covering over 2 square metres to enable the new ridge beam to be inserted into the roof void and reinstatement of roof covering on completion of works.

Plywood web repair to top rafters/ bending ridge board – COST £1080

10.8 SAGGING SINGLE-PITCHED ROOF

Typically this type of roof is found on a single-storey addition for, say, a kitchen or outhouse in an old terraced house.

Many of the roof spans were probably at the span and load limit when originally constructed, and the addition of any new heavier roof covering (the ubiquitous concrete tile again?) will rapidly exacerbate the problem. You will encounter many such roofs, which are badly 'dished' and sagged as a consequence. Even when covered in lighter slate the roof will be prone to sag.

The sagging may not look too drastic until checked against a long straight edge such as a 1.5-m spirit level; the divergence is likely to assume more dramatic proportions when it can be measured rather than simply checked by eye.

Often these roofs have 'skilling' ceilings – that is to say, the ceiling finish is applied directly to the underside of the rafters and there are no separate ceiling joists to restrain the rafter framework. A common result is that the roof starts to slide away – opening up flashings at the external top edge or possibly along the sides of any enclosing walls, and possibly causing the outer wall to buckle as well.

On older properties these roofs tend to be built off half-brick-thick single-storey back addition walls, so it is sensible to consider:

- Is the repair economic, or is it worth reconstructing the whole part of the building to a higher standard?
- Is there any local authority grant available for improvement works as part of the project?

- Are there any other ways of improving the weather resistance of the wall? Examples include:
  - applying an external damp membrane, insulation batts and metal lathing and render; or
  - an internal membrane, insulation batts and a plasterboard finish (care usually needs to be taken however to ensure the floor is also isolated by a DPM or similar, and also to insulate it in many instances, to prevent damp ingress or cold bridging since the old floors are often solid and have no original damp proof membrane).

Solution 1

If the wall plate at the head of the wall is in sound condition it can be fixed or refixed to the wall and a mild steel strap used to lock the rafters to it.

- Check that the tops of the rafters have not been affected by years of moisture trickling through cracked flashings, and that they have adequate bearing and integrity onto the wall plate.

Solution 2

If the wall plate at the head of the wall is decayed or compromised it should be fairly straightforward to 'plate up' the rafters with new timbers screwed up alongside for, say, a metre or so along the length of each affected rafter, and fixed back onto the wall plate.

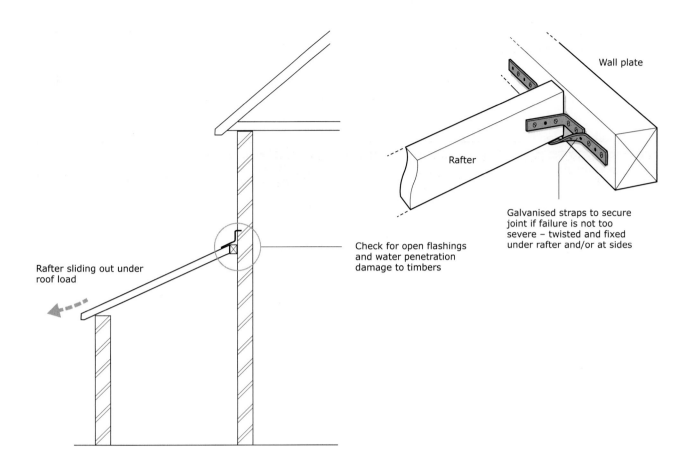

Wall plate

Rafter

Galvanised straps to secure joint if failure is not too severe – twisted and fixed under rafter and/or at sides

Rafter sliding out under roof load

Check for open flashings and water penetration damage to timbers

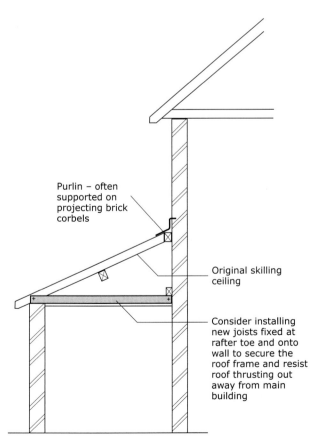

Purlin – often supported on projecting brick corbels

Original skilling ceiling

Consider installing new joists fixed at rafter toe and onto wall to secure the roof frame and resist roof thrusting out away from main building

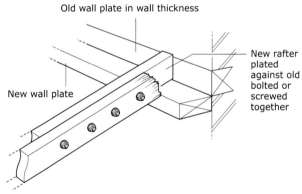

Old wall plate in wall thickness

New rafter plated against old bolted or screwed together

New wall plate

If the existing plate is in this position it is sometimes possible to install a new plate from beneath. Fixing below in 'stiff' section and resin grouting stud bolts may be effective

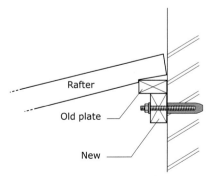

Rafter

Old plate

New

Sometimes the rafters are found to be only resting or leaning onto the wall; sometimes set into sockets in the brickwork.

Solution 3

A new wall plate can be pushed up from underneath and fixed with resin anchors or studding set into polyester resin glue and then bolted in place.

If there is sufficient headroom then a ceiling can be formed on new ceiling joists and the joists can be fixed at each end to restrain the roof – if the span is short enough. If not, then noggings can be used to brace the ceiling joists and binders run over them to tie the rafter feet in.

Solution 4

Where a new ceiling cannot be created, a purlin can be run across the roof in the usual way; if needs be, making a feature of the timber by cleaning it up and finishing it if it has to be exposed through the skilling ceiling.

10.9 OVER-STRESSED OR BROKEN HIP BOARDS

Where a hipped roof has been re-covered, the hip board may well be over-stressed from the increased load. It is likely to buckle, or bend or sometimes snap, because the hip board is usually slender in comparison to the rafter thickness.

Solution

The hip can often be propped and the prop supported in turn on a 'dragon beam' run across the corner of the building. The beam needs to be stiff enough not to bend under the point load imposed by the prop, and needs to be fixed securely so it will not shift under the load or any accidental impact.

Ideally the beam should also be lifted a little above the top of the existing ceiling joists so that if it were to deflect it would be unlikely to press down onto the existing joists.

Consider also, Problem 10.7, Solution 3.

Watch out for ceiling joists, which once restrained the rafters at the end fixings but now do not. A hundred years since the roof was constructed, old fixing nails are likely to have rusted away, amply assisted by shock from wind loads or, in some cases, wartime bomb damage.

Beware of bomb-shock damage

Where bomb shockwave has occurred it is interesting to observe how often the joist overlap at the centre of the building is now gapped or buckled. Occasionally the entire roof frame is displaced across the building by 50 mm or so.

The local library or the local authority's Building Control Department often retain a copy of the war damage record, which can be checked if there is a suspicion that damage of this nature has occurred.

These records were originally maintained to plot valid claims for war damage compensation, but some of those repairs were by necessity of a very immediate nature with building materials in short supply during and immediately after the war, and they may bear careful re-examination.

It can help rule out (or in) damage from other causes such as subsidence or structural failure of the roof frame.

A check of the fixings at rafter feet and ceiling joists and at ceiling joist laps could enable a very cheap, but cost effective, screw fix repair at these nodal points. However, it is important to check the joists where they lap in the centre of the roof – not just the fixings at the eaves.

COST SEQUENCE – Repair to broken hip board

1. Cut pair of plywood webs/gussets to fit triangle of roof space.
2. This repair is only likely to be suitable for repairs to hip boards up to about 2 m in length.
3. Longer lengths will need to be fabricated with built up panels of plywood of sufficient size to be brought through the roof access hatch.
4. Allow for nominally a 2-m run length along the hip board with corresponding right-angled triangles to lower edge and internal edge of web.
5. Cut sockets so that the ply webs can be slid under the existing rafter locations.
6. Construct timber binder in nominally 200 mm by 50 mm section timber spanning from the hip board location to internal load bearing wall if within suitable span, or construct T-beam with hanger spanning from internal/ Party Wall through to adjoining main wall. Add vertical prop in 50 mm section timber to close the inner edge of the ply gusset/sandwich. Slide over defective hip board and allow for stud bolting or screw fixing in shear resistant quality screws at nominally 300 mm centres.

Repair to broken hip board – COST £300

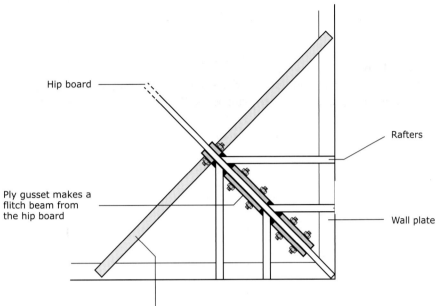

Hip board

Rafters

Ply gusset makes a
flitch beam from
the hip board

Wall plate

Beam picks up part load from bent or broken hip board

Roof hip plywood dragon beam variation in plan

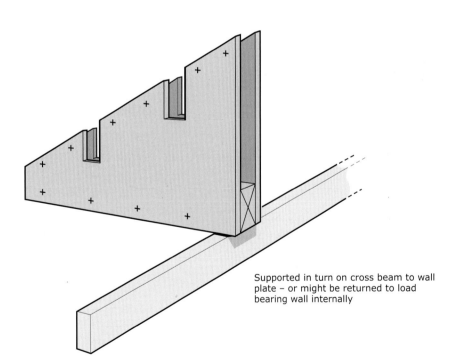

Supported in turn on cross beam to wall
plate – or might be returned to load
bearing wall internally

Ply gusset for hipboard repair

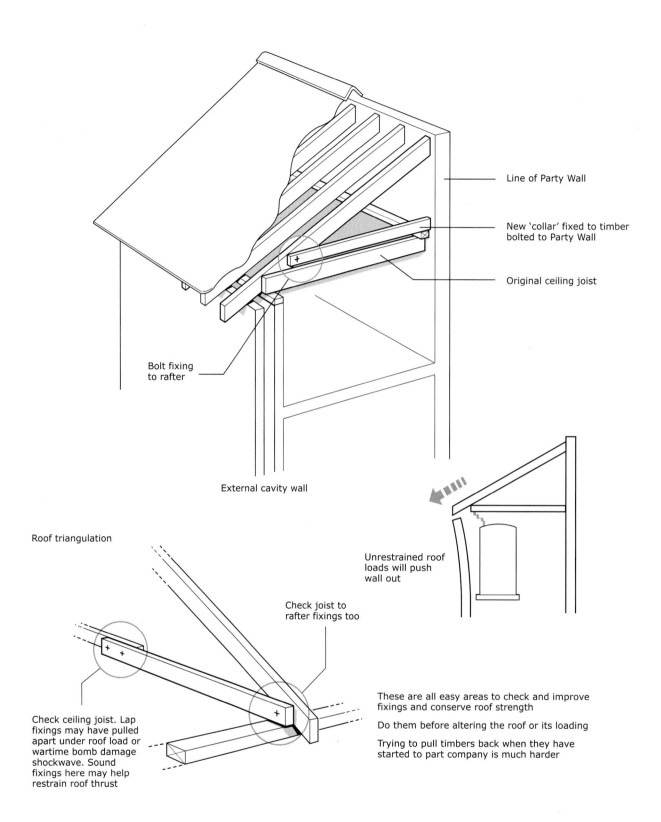

Line of Party Wall

New 'collar' fixed to timber bolted to Party Wall

Original ceiling joist

Bolt fixing to rafter

External cavity wall

Roof triangulation

Unrestrained roof loads will push wall out

Check joist to rafter fixings too

Check ceiling joist. Lap fixings may have pulled apart under roof load or wartime bomb damage shockwave. Sound fixings here may help restrain roof thrust

These are all easy areas to check and improve fixings and conserve roof strength

Do them before altering the roof or its loading

Trying to pull timbers back when they have started to part company is much harder

Roof spread and 'collar' repairs

10.10 UNSUPPORTED PURLIN JOINTS (ALONG THE LENGTH OF THE PURLIN)

Sometimes the original detailing of the roof is compromised. It is not unusual to find a purlin jointed along its length but supported only on the 'top' joint side. A new heavier roof covering will soon find this out. The detail is illustrated right, top. (Once you start looking for this type of defect when carrying out building and roof repairs you will be amazed at how often it is encountered.)

Solution

A simple plated repair bolting a large section of timber across the joint should be adequate in most cases in this situation (shown right, bottom).

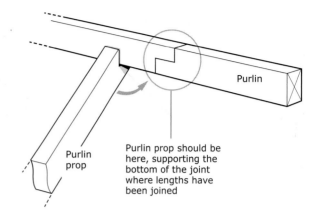

Purlin

Purlin prop

Purlin prop should be here, supporting the bottom of the joint where lengths have been joined

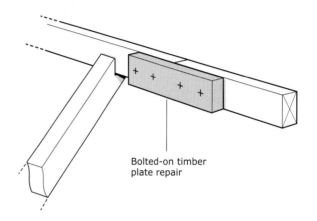

Bolted-on timber plate repair

10.11 HALF-BRICK-THICK GABLES

Older pitched roofs may have a half-brick skin to the gable triangle; even though the wall beneath the roof or ceiling joist level is in fact of cavity masonry construction.

Solution

Double check this: if you are putting in new purlins you will need to raise an inner skin of brickwork at least sufficient for the purlin to rest on.

A full cavity thickness is desirable because a half-brick gable may be susceptible to wind load or suction, particularly if the pointing is of any age. Many such walls failed in the great storm of 1987, and a stitch in time would have offered considerable reinforcement to many of these.

10.12 DAMP PENETRATION IN A ROOF

If there is no obvious route for water entry, check the tile gauge, i.e. that there is sufficient lap for the specification and size of tile being used (sometimes there is a temptation for the roofer to open up the gauge and save a little bit of money and weight). You will need a long ladder to investigate, unless you can pull away a section of roofing felt from inside the roof (which obviously usually needs permission from the owner).

As well as resisting driven water penetration and helping to even-out wind loads through the roof, the felt laps into the gutter to prevent accelerated decay to the timbers beneath. However, traditional felts can soon decay from solar exposure, causing the edge lapped into the gutter to deteriorate. There is a proprietary plastic eaves detail now available from some of the u-PVC window and cladding manufacturers, and this profile can be sleeved under a deteriorated felt edge and into the gutter if only a small and relatively localised felt repair is needed.

Where there is a particularly aggressive and wet climate, counter-battening helps to ensure any driven rainwater is drained away over the felt should it penetrate under the slate covering. This would also reduce the risk of the battens rotting should moisture become trapped between any poorly set sections of roofing felt which may be trapped under a conventional roofing batten.

Remember, though; the tile gauge should be adjusted to prevent driven rain penetration. The felt will help protect the roof from moisture, but its primary function is to control the effects of wind load and suction on and through the roof.

10.13 PONDING ON A FLAT ROOF

Initial checks should verify:

- Has the deck beneath sunk?
- Was it even laid to a meaningful drainage fall in the first place?
- Are the outlets or secret gutter/downpipes well detailed?

Occasionally roofs have been re-covered when the felt was sound but the outlet pipes were blocked and water consequently backed up under the felt. I have even seen schemes where the outlets and downpipes do not align, causing water to shed into the building.

Why check the roofing deck? Well, a variety of interesting materials have been used over the last 40 years, and some perform very indifferently.

Cement/strawboard or chipboard has all the qualities of soggy paper once water has got in. You need to establish if you are only recovering with a new layer of felt or if one deck has been applied over a perished old one, when a complete re-deck will be required.

Sometimes it is worth taking a core sample through the felt. This can establish:

- the type of roofing felt
- whether the roof covering (felt or felt and decking) has been applied directly over the top of an old failed covering (or failed deck).

Solution 1 (temporary)

A temporary solution could be to repair a felt flat roof (or asphalt) using a glass-reinforced plastic (GRP) 'pour on' finish to seal the old roof, or by patching the original material over any cracks or leaks.

GRP is reasonably effective – nevertheless, treatments such as these are weak at sharp corners, arrises, and the like, and will still be at risk if there is much pedestrian traffic, for example, where a flat roof deck serves as access to flat conversions, or where there are balconies or perhaps unauthorised roof gardens to flats. (The cast iron chair legs soon leave telltale marks punching through the deck, despite the tenants denying that they have a barbecue on the roof every weekend in the summer!)

Solution 2

When re-covering, it makes sense to look at and coordinate options to improve roof insulation.

The traditional fibreglass quilt laid in the roof void formed by the flat roof joists has limited efficiency. An air gap is still required to ventilate the roof, and the insulation soon becomes a soggy mess once water gets in, which it inevitably does sooner or later.

Before you write the specification, ensure that there is sufficient upstand for the roof covering, and look at improving this within the specification if appropriate. For example, if the roof has a secret gutter and it becomes blocked, then ideally the ponding rainwater should flow through some form of warning gully or similar outlet before it backs up and around the cover flashings and into the building fabric.

- Ideally any upstands should be a minimum of 150 mm with a cover flashing of 100 mm or more turned over.

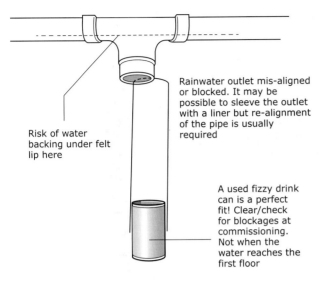

Risk of water backing under felt lip here

Rainwater outlet mis-aligned or blocked. It may be possible to sleeve the outlet with a liner but re-alignment of the pipe is usually required

A used fizzy drink can is a perfect fit! Clear/check for blockages at commissioning. Not when the water reaches the first floor

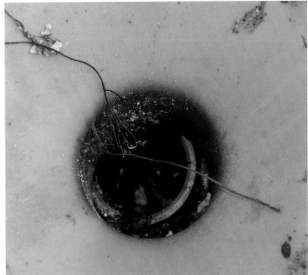

I wish I had kept a record of the number of fizzy drinks cans and polystyrene cups I have retrieved from downpipes!

Flat roof under a foot of water

I recall lifting the trap onto a five-storey office block flat roof only to discover that it was under about a foot of water (about 300 mm). Any higher and the water would have flowed down the access trap or into the plant room lift shaft.

Unbelievably the strawboard roof deck held up under the massive weight imposed on it and the roof covering was fairly sound – a couple of pin prick leaks had raised the alarm early.

The cost of disruption to the business if the roof had emptied itself through the building hardly bears thinking about.

Would the building designer have been liable for this poor original detail? I don't know the answer. This design was common when the building was constructed. Or would the tenants have been liable for failure to maintain and inspect regularly?

Roofs are frequently repaired on a like-for-like basis, but it makes sense to improve them if possible.

10.14 REDUCED FLASHING CLEARANCES

This can be a problem if you are adding a new, thicker deck to accommodate new insulation. It may then be necessary to adjust the DPC and cover flashing levels to re-coordinate them, unless they are already sufficiently generous.

Solution

The old cover flashing clearances may well need resetting to allow for this. It is usually a futile exercise to try to leave the original flashings in place unless there is plenty of room to spare. Ensure that contractors are not inclined to take a shortcut in this respect if you are checking the works.

10.15 FAILURE OF ASBESTOS CEMENT SHEET

Asbestos cement sheet covering probably lasts about 40 years or thereabouts, and many estates where it has been used will now be either due for demolition or ready for the roof to be re-covered.

Given the problems of handling and disposal of asbestos-based materials, any re-roofing operation can no longer be considered cheap, and use of a licensed contractor may well be required if the material is in particularly poor condition and likely to lead to excess fibre and dust release.

The Control of Asbestos at Work Regulations 2006 stipulate fibre release limits, which will govern the appropriate protocol for stripping off this type of material, and you then have the problem of considering what is the appropriate replacement.

Both asbestos cement sheets and sheet metal roofing are prone to leakage around the fixings.

'J' bolts were commonly used for asbestos cement sheets, and either 'J' bolts or self-tapping roofing sheet screws commonly used for profiled metal sheet roofing are prone to failures, especially when the neoprene seating washers give way (or are omitted).

All of these rely on the correct tension/torsion being applied to the fixing screw, and over-tightening will rapidly rip through the neoprene washer which provides the water seal under the nut head on the top surface of the roof. Over-tightening can either fracture the sheet covering (fibre cement materials) or buckle the sheet covering (metal sheeting), all leading to increased risk of localised water penetration.

Solution 1

The fixing methodology and workmanship is critical for any sort of sheet roof material. There are no shortcuts on this one! Check to confirm that the self-tapping or other fixings have been properly secured and that neoprene washers are intact.

Solution 2

There are modern fibre-reinforced cement replacement products which replicate many of the profiles of the corrugated asbestos cement sheet roofing, though the longevity of these materials has yet to be established, in my opinion.

Re-covering will often be carried out using a substitute profiled sheet metal with a plastic polymer coating. Again these are relatively lightweight sheets and should not adversely affect roof loading significantly where they replace an asbestos fibre cement product, but it would always be prudent to have the loading characteristics of the roof checked prior to re-covering.

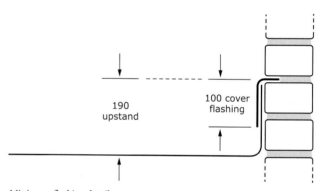

190 upstand

100 cover flashing

Minimum flashing details

10.16 CONDENSATION UNDER ASBESTOS CEMENT OR SHEET METAL ROOF

Asbestos cement roofs and particularly profiled sheet metal roofing can be prone to heavy condensation build-up on the underside of the roof. Consequently it is common to find insulation board applied to the underside of the roof.

In properties constructed before about the mid-1990s there is a high chance that this will contain a degree of asbestos. Considerable care is required (see Problem 10.15).

Solution

Over- or under-cladding/lining may effect a temporary solution. That is to say, old materials can be left in place and a new suspended ceiling or insulation lining fitted over.

You must ensure that appropriate records are kept to identify the material hidden beneath, and you should design any solution with an eye on the future so that everything can be safely removed later – particularly if asbestos-containing materials (ACMs) have been covered over. Maintenance teams will need to know of its presence.

Appropriate detailing for health and safety can substantially increase the cost even if the insulation layer is not apparently defective at present.

10.17 DETERIORATION OF PCM

Plastic coated metal (PCM) finishes will deteriorate over time.

Solution

The roof can be stripped and re-coated.

If encouraged by the client to refurbish a building in the corporate colours, it may be necessary to make them aware that reinstatement to the original colour and finish is necessary again at some considerable potential cost at the end of a lease.

10.18 FIRE CHECKS AT PARTY WALLS

When re-roofing pitched roofs – particularly on semi-detached or terraced houses – you need to take account of the risk of fire spread.

Solution

A mortar fire stopping should be applied to close the voids left by the roofing battens over the top of the Party Wall. Depending on the extent and location of the work, you may well need to issue a Party Wall Notice. Section 2 sub-section 2 of the Party Wall etc. Act describes the various scenarios which apply in this instance.

10.19 ROOF FELTS AND INSULATION/VAPOUR RESISTANCE

Modern building practices should operate on the principle of 'built tight; ventilate right', but specifications do not always pay sufficient attention to the need for ventilation, resulting in buildings being effectively sealed, with consequential build-up of moisture.

Solution

Some forms of insulating roofing felts have been recently introduced, but again care needs to be taken when specifying, and a couple of underlay types were introduced and very rapidly withdrawn when found to be comparatively ineffective.

- Ensure that an appropriate grade of breathable fabric has been used for the roof.
- Care also needs to be taken in specifying underlays to ensure that there is a sufficient vapour resistance.

10.20 FIXING HIP TILES

Correct fixing of hip tiles is essential; but wet fixing methods are not always secure.

Solution

Pay careful attention to hip details:

- When inspecting the roof, the hip iron securing the hip tiles at the bottom of the slope may appear to be sound but it often turns out to be completely defective – an accident waiting to happen. The tiles could slide off the roof under the next high wind.

When specifying, it is important to ensure that hip irons are checked and properly secured, and that all hip tiles are likewise properly secured in a cement bedding or, if necessary, with a mechanical fixing.

Consider using a dry fixing system. This may be both lighter and more secure. There are several systems on the market, and some incorporate an under-flashing membrane for additional protection from driven rain.

10.21 WATER PENETRATION AT WALL ABUTMENTS WITH ROOFS

This is very common, and is usually the result of basic detailing errors.

Solution

Where parapet walls are involved, it is essential to check the workmanship; there seems to be huge scope for lack of attention to the right details in this area.

Ensure the contractor is aware of Building Regulation requirements and of good practice details such as those in *Rolled Lead Sheet – The Complete Manual* (June 2007) published by the Lead Sheet Association (*www.leadsheetassociation.org.uk*).

On-site supervision by the surveyor in areas such as this can more than pay off in terms of saved hours later trying to inspect and resolve the problem after the scaffold has been removed.

New-build; new waterfall

I recall a particular problem on a new-build new roof where there was a backfall in the felt under the tiles before it dropped into the parapet taper gutter (sometimes wrongly called a 'box gutter'). This discharged onto the internal wall of the parapet some 100 mm (4 inches) deep. It was just waiting to fill up with water before it eventually poured back into the building.

A complete re-roof was the only solution, because the levels of the roof sheeting and battening were completely wrong.

Although the roofing contractor was extremely resistant, nevertheless re-roofing was the only solution in the end.

Sometimes you really do have to stick to your guns. In this case, it helped that the client was prepared to litigate.

COST SEQUENCE – Roof eaves felt repair

Supply appropriate access. Ladder or scaffold tower assumed for pricing purposes, two-storey height assumed. Assumed eaves run of 6 m.

1. Carefully strip back lower 2 no. courses of tiles at eaves and set aside for re-use.
2. Carefully cut back defective roofing felt at eaves lap into gutter.
3. Allow for breaking out of the lowest roofing/tile batten.
4. Install propriety u-PVC eaves of flashing detail spiked to top face of rafters and re-dress original felt over lap.
5. Reinstate new lowest tile batten.
6. Re-set 2 courses of tile to original gauge.

Roof eaves felt repair – COST £390

Chapter 11
Floors and flooring

The vast majority of floor repairs you are likely to encounter will relate to timber floors, although there are a few interesting and relatively common solid floor problems too. And in my experience, timber floor repair issues fall into a fairly limited range of typical scenarios – collapse of a suspended timber ground floor being the most common.

KEY CONSIDERATIONS

It is difficult to persuade Building Owners to allow the necessary time, cost and disturbance to carry out comprehensive checks when flooring repairs are necessary. The current vogue (at the time of writing) for applying laminate flooring also reduces the scope for checks beneath the boards. But checks are well worth it in the long run.

Use of a Protimeter™ hammer probe to take moisture readings at some depth in the joist ends is certainly worth considering. The probes can also be hammered through floorboards if you do not have permission to lift floor coverings; but be aware that the 50–60 mm probe depth may only provide limited information, and it is probably unwise to rely on it in isolation.

- ◆ **Ensure that you are quite clear about the scope of the inspection when confirming terms of engagement, and make the Building Owners/clients quite aware of the risk of a limited inspection.**

For ground floor work:

- ◆ **Remember to allow for continuity of sub-floor ventilation. (Solid floors can easily block and interrupt airflows to other parts of the building. So too can new walls and partitions; even if they are vented, the loss of airflow may be critical in a large building.)**

- ◆ **If there is a cellar or basement beneath the main timber ground floor, you may need to consider repairs in the manner of a first floor, but with added regard again to protecting the ends of any joists or wall plates which might come into contact with the comparatively high risk band of wall at the damp proof course/ground level intersection.**

- ◆ **In some cases it will be necessary to incorporate a suitable membrane to resist radon gas. This can be complicated; and careful detailing at the perimeter of the walls/floors is generally required to prevent any routes for ingress of radon gas. Sometimes a secondary radon barrier on the oversite is also required in addition to a ventilated void.**

In Chapter 9 (Walls) we stressed the importance of using lime mortar joints and pointing where these were the original jointing materials. This is even more important where there are solid walls and joists have been built into or rest upon them. Portland cement pointing can rapidly elevate the moisture content of the wall and trigger problems such as wet or dry rot in the joist end bearings (which could spread rapidly).

First floor joists can suffer end bearing problems too. For example, the original bearing could be inadequate, or damp penetration through a solid wall could cause deterioration of the timber over time. Frequently, poorly executed alterations, such as notching for heating pipes, causes weaknesses to develop. In the former, the cure is generally similar to that detailed above.

When carrying out refurbishment and alteration works I would also make a plea for careful detailing of pipe runs where these necessarily have to be embedded within the floor – preferably using some form of proprietary ducting, rather than casting the pipes into the floor.

Where this must be done, then it is imperative that suitable lagging is put round the pipe to reduce risk of both condensation and damage to the service pipes. (The cost, disturbance and upset caused by having to dig out defective service pipes embedded in the screed is considerable.)

The box, Floors – the basics, should serve as a useful aide memoire when you are out on a site inspection.

FLOORS – THE BASICS

Timber floors

The most common types include:

- timber ground floors on traditional sleeper walls
- traditional suspended timber joist first floor/ upper floors
- floated floors, i.e. a timber deck faced onto a concrete base or similar
- unventilated suspended timber basement floors (older properties).

Concrete block-and-beam floors

This method of construction is very similar to a traditional suspended timber floor but incorporates a series of inverted T concrete reinforced beams which are infilled with concrete blocks before screeding over.

In the context of this book it is unlikely that you will be carrying out the detailed design of a concrete block-and-beam floor. Instead, most manufacturers will be able to supply you with the necessary specification and construction information for their particular version of the product, including beam strength calculations for Building Control submissions/ approval. Despite the perceived strength of concrete, it is possible for the beams to be over-loaded, so you do need to ensure that you have provided them with sufficient information about the position of any partition walls, and any extra loads being applied (e.g. from floors above, the roof, or any lintels which pick up openings, spans or loads from elsewhere in the building). You will also need to ensure that the beam positions are marked out correctly (e.g. on the adjacent wall) so that they can be referenced after the floor screed has been laid, and partitions correctly aligned on them.

The concrete is rather more resistant to decay from condensation than timber would be (certainly in the absence of contaminants or incompatible ground conditions), but it is still appropriate to maintain a sensible air gap under the floor and to ensure there is adequate ventilation to prevent the build up of condensation.

Any form of suspended timber floor or concrete floor will offer advantages, particularly on sites which are very out of level. The concrete suspended floor also presents the opportunity for incorporating insulation beneath the screed.

The requirements of the Building Regulations are changing rapidly (especially regarding energy conservation, and the control and minimisation of acoustic transmission), so the specification of this type of floor can become increasingly complex. Early dialogue with some of the manufacturers and suppliers is strongly recommended so that a cost/specification can be considered at an early stage.

Concrete wide span beams will require similarly careful treatment.

Reinforced concrete floors

These are probably most commonly encountered in commercial premises, and incorporate a traditional steel reinforcing mesh within a cast concrete floor.

Again, this floor type can be subject to over-loading, and it is extremely difficult to assess what the original load-bearing characteristics of the floor would have been. Sometimes it is necessary to actually break open a section of the concrete in order to examine the depth of the reinforcing bars or mesh and also to consider the size and dimensioning of the reinforcing material before an accurate assessment can be made of the floor's load-bearing capacity.

With the tendency towards paperless offices and more electronic communications there should be less loading on modern commercial floors – in theory – nevertheless, the need to store large quantities of material to avoid litigation in the future could risk overburdening the floor slab.

Repairs or modifications to this type of floor are best specified by an appropriately experienced Building Surveyor or structural engineer, but you need to be in a position to consider the implications of this.

Ground-supported floor slabs

Essentially this means the concrete is cast directly onto the ground.

Some form of damp proof material needs to be incorporated, but this is a frequent cause of failure. Older solid floors may indeed have no damp proof membrane at all; many have perforated membranes because of sharp rubble in the hardcore base.

The early damp proof membranes would have incorporated a brushed-on layer of bitumen. This would have probably also been painted around the wall perimeters to coincide with the main damp proof course. Conveniently this solution would have also created a low-friction area helping the floor to settle down inside the perimeter walls.

Magnesite composition flooring

Occasionally you may come across 'magnesite composition flooring' (sometimes known as 'jointless flooring). This is a combination of magnesium oxychloride together with a bulking agent (typically sawdust, but a number of other products were used, including asbestos).

The floor generally has an ochre yellow tint but could also have other colourings. It suffers dramatically if it becomes damp, and although this floor type is primarily used in commercial premises nevertheless it is sometimes also encountered in domestic properties. Prevalent in the 1920s and '30s, it was used in a few cases until the 1950s.

PROBLEMS – FLOORS AND FLOORING

11.1 COLLAPSED SUSPENDED TIMBER GROUND FLOOR

At first the problem is hardly noticeable – a little springing in the floor perhaps; then a little more vibration; then the ornaments on the television start to wobble as you walk past! (Eventually the TV may topple over – it does happen!)

The most advanced case I ever saw involved a thick rug, which was the only thing that prevented one from wading ankle deep through the floorboards.

The usual cause is lack of sub-floor ventilation; older properties, especially in England (the Scots were well ahead of us on this one) generally having no over-site finish applied to avoid moisture evaporation under the floor (and condensation).

If you are lucky, the joists or floorboards will only have gone soft; possibly there may be some wet rot.

If the defect is as simple as that, then repairs are usually straightforward. The minimum being to improve the sub-floor ventilation and replace the defective timbers.

However, it would be risky to assume that there are no other contributory factors. So an investigation is essential:

- Check the gaps between the brick sleeper walls are clear. (The floor void is frequently used as a free skip by passing builders, especially on refurbishment projects. Is this a building which has been builder modernised?)
- Check the joist ends. Has the damp proof course (DPC) been compromised on the main walls externally (or internally)? Is there a render finish, cement plinth, a new patio or footpath? Has it bridged the DPC? If air vents have been blocked the DPC has probably been bridged too. Even if the DPC is not fully covered up, a reduced clearance can trigger surprising amounts of damp ingress as rain splashes off ground surface finishes.
- Does the patio or path drain back towards the house? Even if the air vents are not bridged they may well fill up if the patio floods and water is being dumped into the floor void.
- Check for dry rot – even if in the early stages. This can be a very hard one to detect if there is no full-blown outbreak. The new Fugenex™ detectors marketed by RICS Books (see *www.surveyors-equipment.com*) may prove particularly useful allies in monitoring any repairs.
- Check the condition of water service pipes. Old lead water pipes can develop tiny pinhole leaks as they age. A small fountain of water may well have been erupting under the floorboards for some time before a problem is noticed. If the joist ends are affected it might also be the neighbour's water pipe which is leaking onto a Party Wall, and should be considered if the pipework proves sound in the affected property.

- Check that any heating pipes are not leaking. This may involve running the system up if it is dormant during the summer months in order to make suitable checks.
- A quick check to see if there have been any historic floods or water leaks (burst pipes, tanks in roofs etc.) which have been cured but without proper drying out elsewhere.

You may find (particularly in cottages) that the walls step in thickness – the ledge forming a bearing for the upper floor joists. For example, it is not uncommon in Surrey to find a 215-mm (9-inch) ground floor wall and a tile-hung half brick thick first floor wall. Occasionally the first floor main walls are of timber construction with tile hanging. It would pay to check that the joist end bearings are suitably stiffened where they rest on the ledge with nogging pieces to reduce the risk of the timbers twisting under load, which could weaken the bearing position.

Once you have established that there are no hidden extra contributory factors to the problem, then it should be safe to proceed with a repair.

Solution 1

If the timbers are affected and have softened or decayed but there is no rot, then it should be safe to replace with like for like. A sensible extra precaution is to sleeve a layer of modern plastic DPC material on top of the sleeper wall and beneath any timber plates or joists.

Builders' merchants and DIY stores now sell small plastic wedges to help with levelling up new joists to old for a perfect repair. But it should be a simple matter for a builder to make up timber wedges on site, and

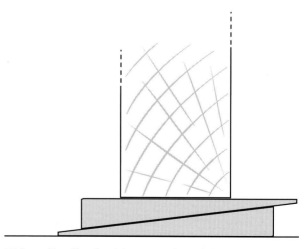

Folding or 'French' wedges: it is easy to make quick changes to levels by tapping the wedges 'in' or 'out' against each others.

opposed or 'French' wedges are a quick and traditional way of making even fairly large changes to level by tapping the wedges in or out.

If joist or plate ends have been affected by decay it is sensible, too, to wrap the new joist in some DPC to isolate them from any future damp risk.

Ensure rubble from under the floor is cleared out, bagged carefully and disposed of offsite. This will eliminate the slightest risk of spreading any dry rot spores (or any other rot, for that matter).

COST SEQUENCE – Repairs to timber ground floor

1. Carefully remove existing skirting boards and set aside for re-use.
2. Assumed floor size/room size 5 m by 5 m.
3. Break out existing floorboard covering. Condition is assumed to be poor and re-use not feasible.
4. Carefully break out existing joists/wall plates assumed to be sat on sleeper wall construction.
5. Cut down all timber lengths and carefully bag up and cart away to minimise risk of dust or spore contamination, even if dry rot or other fungal defects not identified.
6. Clear out spaces in between existing honey-comb sleeper walls. Allow for 1 cubic metre of cart-way debris.
7. Ensure all existing under-floor ventilator bricks are un-obstructed and operating satisfactorily.
8. Lay PVC damp-proof course material across the top of all sleeper walls. Fix down new timber plates nominal dimensions 100 mm by 50 mm treated softwood assumed. Allow for levelling of plate using proprietary plastic folding wedges/slips.
9. Reinstate floor using 22 mm floor grade chipboard. Allow for all appropriate cutting in.
10. Re-fix skirting boards, caulk all joints at mitres. Bring forward, 2 undercoat and 1 top white gloss assumed.

Repairs to timber ground floor – COST £1700 without floor insulation: £2300 with floor insulation

---

Solution 2

One of the most straightforward repair strategies is to bolt a steel angle section to the wall, but giving some added consideration to:

- how to protect the joist ends from damp walls
- how to conceal the steel angle, if appropriate.

Solution 3

Although they cannot prevent a sagging floor from continuing to sag, noggings are extremely functional, and the cross-bracing and stiffening effect may be very beneficial in helping to arrest any further movement (perhaps in conjunction with a scheme to double up the joists to spread existing loads).

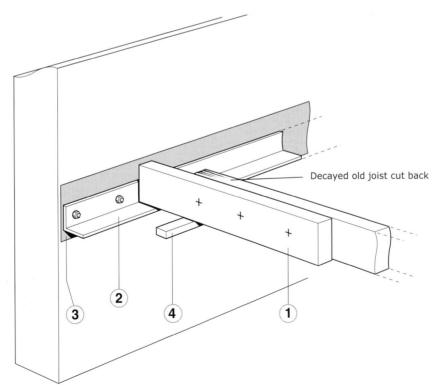

Floor joist repair (decayed old joist cut back): (1) 'plated up' floor joist; (2) Consider counter-batten to drop new ceiling line OR notch plated joist to set it to original joist line (notched over 'shelf') and re-make ceiling to original level; (3) Plastic DPC roll to isolate steel and timber from damp solid wall; (4) Steel angle shelf fixed by resin-socketed stud bolts or chemical anchor.

COST SEQUENCE – Inserting noggings

1. Assumed floor 4 m by 4 m suspended timber joist.
2. Carefully lift all floorboard coverings and set aside for re-use.
3. Cut timber block nogging pieces slightly short of the joist depth so that these do not interfere with the existing ceiling fabric.
4. Insert 2 no. nogging pieces between each joist centre at approximately 1 m from the end bearing of each joist. Allow for screw fixing only, with skewed in screws to prevent vibration damage to plaster and ceiling surfaces below. Ensure service runs are not interrupted.
5. Reinstate floorboard covering with all boards screwed back into place.

NB: No allowance has been made for reinstatement of damaged chipboard coverings where this finish is in place.

6. Allow for localised making good to flush off proud edges to floorboards leaving in clean sound and splinter free condition. Use of butt edge floorboards (not tongue and grove boards) is assumed.

Insert noggings – COST £340

11.2 UNDERSIZED FLOOR JOISTS

The floor joists in older properties, especially pre-1880 or thereabouts, are frequently undersized when compared with modern building standards. To make matters worse, these days we tend to have more furniture (in the case of dwellings) or more boxes and filing cabinets (to store records in case of future litigation) in the case of commercial properties.

Joist hangers are sometimes retrofitted to provide support for new doubled-up joist timbers inserted midway between the original joists to help redistribute the floor load.

But a steel angle shelf is a means of providing added bearing surface to the existing joists at the same time and to my mind is to be preferred, especially if there is a risk of hidden joist end decay. This can be used in a similar manner to that shown in Problem 11.1, Solution 2 (above).

COST SEQUENCE – First floor joist repair/ support

Assumes first or second floor joists can be improved with no special access requirements.

Assumes that screw-jack support can be installed from the ground to first floor with no requirement for special/ additional reinforcement apart from timber spreader plates.

For first floor joist repair:

1. Screw-jack supports installed at 2 m centres to about 1.5 m back from the joist ends/wall with timber spreader plates taken across ground floor and at ceiling level to provide temporary support to the floor.
2. Break out ceiling finish up to 1 m from the existing wall/joist bearings.
3. Floorboards and floor covering to be carefully removed 1.5 m or more away from the floor above to expose top and bottom of the joists. Carefully set aside for re-use.
4. Carefully cut away decayed joist ends. Allow for removal of any decayed waste joist ends within voids in the wall.
5. Plate up decayed joist ends and allow for new sections of timber, say 1.3 m in length bolt fixed along side the original joists with minimum no. 4 bolt fixings (assumes use of engineering stud bolts, washers and nuts on each side).

6. Minimum stud bolt size: M15.
7. Sleeve PVC damp-proof course material across the joist ends to prevent any contact with damp solid wall surfaces.
8. Slide in steel angle shelf with minimum 75 mm bearing edge for the new joist ends.
9. Assumes new supporting stud bolts are socketed into the wall at 400 mm centres, secured in resin fixings with steel angle shelf bolted in place. (Fixing positions will need to be adjusted to fit around assumed 400 mm joists centres.) Structural engineer to calculate/verify fixity method, if any doubt as to masonry support capacity. NOT INCLUDED IN THIS COSTING
10. Replace skirting boards and floor boards above and screw back down onto floor and allow for any flushing off and any tidying up.
11. Remake repaired ceiling finish below. Allow for 12.5 mm plasterboard with joints set and flushed. Allow for 2 coats matt white paint to entire ceiling of assumed area 25 square metres.

First floor joist repair – COST £1400

11.3 OVER-CUT JOISTS

Notching of the joists to accommodate central heating pipes or electrical cable runs is a further cause of joist bending and deflection. Sometimes this can be repaired without resort to joist doubling.

Frequently, however, the joists will have been butchered and the notches will be too large or in the wrong place and will affect the load-bearing capacity of the joist or beam.

Guidance is set out in *Span tables for solid timber floors, ceiling and roofs (especially trussed rafter roofs) for dwellings,* (cited in Building Regulations Approved Document A) and *Timber joist and deck floors – avoiding movement,* Information Sheet 1/36, both published by TRADA (*www.trada.co.uk*).

For joists up to 250 mm the maximum hole should be a quarter of the joist depth and holes should only be drilled in the joist between 0.25 and 0.4 times the span of the joist.

Where the top edge of the joist is notched, the notching should only be carried out in a zone starting at 0.07 times the span, up to 0.25 times the span and to a maximum depth of 1/8 of the joist. Holes and notches should not be overlapped and should be kept at least 100 mm apart.

Solution

Assess the amount of any bending that has already occurred. Often it will not be possible to rectify any sagging to the floor – only to reinforce the structure by way of damage limitation.

This can be achieved by bolting a new joist of approximately similar depth alongside. I say "approximately similar" because if there is a lath and plaster ceiling, for example, then the plaster which has oozed through the timber lathing means that it will be very hard to set a new full-depth timber snugly alongside unless the ceiling is completely taken down first – which is of course an option.

Hopefully the original joist end bearing is sound and it should be a simple matter to 'plate' the defective timber by bolting the new piece alongside (as shown in the sketch which accompanies Problem 11.1, Solution 2).

At least three or four bolts are needed in this situation, and to spread loadings adequately across the notched part a new piece of at least 1.5 m length is preferable – more would probably be called for.

The new joist will need to be notched too but less drastically, or if you are careful the hole drilled in the null load section of the joist may be usable, depending on how badly the old timber has been cut away.

When plating up old joists or doubling them up it would be sensible to insert nogging pieces to help stiffen the structure and provide adequate 'blocking' to help resist twisting as the timbers are put under load.

Flitch beams

An alternative to plating up the joist is to construct a flitch beam. This incorporates a steel plate sandwiched between two conventional timber joists, which are bolted through typically at 300–400 mm centres or less.

Although constructing a flitch beam is a straightforward operation, tolerances can be fine and difficult to prove using conventional rules of thumb. So, in critical applications it is only sensible to have the loading values and stiffness of the beam checked or specified by a structural engineer.

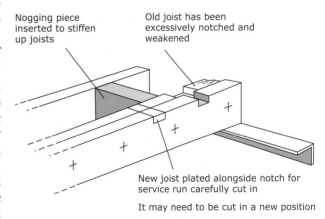

Nogging piece inserted to stiffen up joists

Old joist has been excessively notched and weakened

New joist plated alongside notch for service run carefully cut in

It may need to be cut in a new position

Repair to excessively notched joists.

11.4 SETTLING OF CONCRETE FLOOR SLAB

Once settling starts to occur as ground conditions consolidate or due to seasonal changes in soil volume (particularly on clay soils), then it can be very difficult to consider an appropriate and effective remedial solution.

Solution 1

In particularly bad cases (for example, on a sloping site where there is poorly consolidated hard core under the floor, and where the sloping site means there is more hardcore on one side than another) some very considerable floor movements can occur.

In the worst cases it may be necessary to grub out the floor entirely, consolidate the below ground area using, for example, micro-piles on which to support a new cast floor slab. Obviously this is an expensive solution, but the problem should not then reoccur.

Solution 2 – patch repair

Sometimes where the floor is settling or moving out of true it may only be necessary to apply a new layer of screed to re-level the floor surface every 20 years or so.

Vacuum cleaners give bad vibrations
One engineer of my acquaintance has accounted for many of these floor slabs dropping because of the vibrating rotary action of upright vacuum cleaners, which can set up a resonance through the floor, encouraging it to slide down inside the comparatively low-friction bitumen damp course painted onto the wall within which the floor has been cast.

Bear in mind also that if the DPC is not operating properly – either because the bitumen has not been properly applied, or due to a lack of sand blinding to cover over any sharp edges in the hardcore (any plastic membrane having been punctured as a result) – then moisture penetrating from below can cause the concrete to deteriorate under certain circumstances.

This is sometimes due to contamination from ground water, e.g. if there is soil contamination causing chloride attack on the concrete or other chemical salt attack, perhaps lack of sulfate resisting cement within the mix and so on; all these contaminants can cause significant breakdown in the floor.

Again in these situations it is probably easier to break out the floor and replace it with a properly detailed and specified modern equivalent rather than repair the damage. You will need to consider the value and use of the building in arriving at a decision.

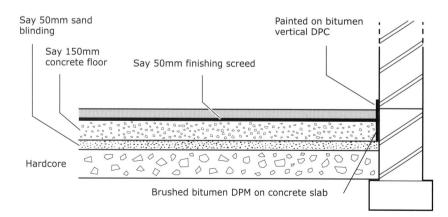

Typical ground-supported slab, with older bitumen DPM detail.

Say 50mm sand blinding

Say 150mm concrete floor

Say 50mm finishing screed

Painted on bitumen vertical DPC

Hardcore

Brushed bitumen DPM on concrete slab

1 The floor slab may settle down inside the low friction vertical DPC painted on the inside wall face

2 Poor aggregate/finishing of the concrete floor or inadequate detailing to brushed-on DPM may allow water ingress due to vapour pressure from the ground

3 Ground contaminants may breakdown the concrete – and the brushed on DPM, e.g. if sulfate resisting cement has not been used in the mix, and there is a high level of natural sulfate contamination in the ground – or aggregate

---

COST SEQUENCE – Defective and settled concrete ground floor (ground supported) slab

1. Assumed ground floor area for typical semi-detached house (i) 15 m by 10 m elevation dimensions, and (ii) 5 m by 10 m plan.
2. Remove all skirting boards, floor coverings and cart away.
3. Carefully breakout existing floor slab and remove hard core.
4. No allowance has been made for finding any contaminative materials within the hard core, e.g. old asbestos or other old building products.
5. Set aside hard core for re-use.
6. Using transportable rig set micro-piles – nominal 100 mm diameter steel tube piles to a depth of 2 m from pile cap to assumed load bearing/friction position. At 2 m centres.
7. Set pile caps.
8. Reinstate hard core to form suitable surface for casting of new floor.
9. Pour in new floor in concrete mix to top of pile cap.
10. New floor assumed minimum 80 mm polystyrene insulation and 60 mm screed with 2000 gauge polythene DPM inserted and terminated at main DPC alignment.
11. Install new skirting boards and allow for 1 coat primer, 2 undercoat and 1 top coat.

Defective and settled concrete ground floor (ground supported) slab – (i) COST £28,000; and (ii) £9500.

11.5 DESICCATED COMPOSITION FLOOR SCREED

It is possible for a magnesite composition floor screed to desiccate (powders and cracks) as it deteriorates with age, and this is rapidly accelerated if it becomes damp.

Solution

This type of floor screed inherently has a limited lifespan, and so it is usually removed if encountered as part of a refurbishment or alteration project. Certainly, any traces should be removed if a kitchen or bathroom is to be located in an area which previously had this type of flooring (and it originally would normally have been kept well away from potentially damp areas, i.e. kept within bedrooms or reception rooms in domestic situations).

You should have the floor sampled to establish whether there is any asbestos content before carrying out further works.

Inherently the floor generally triggers a high damp reading if tested with a traditional conductance moisture meter, usually because of the timber sawdust content holding a large amount of moisture bound within it. (This fact may help you to identify the material in the first place.) Also, testing with one of the proprietary salts testing kits (for magnesium salts) may assist in interpretation.

This type of floor is also prone to sweating sometimes, as it gives out moisture under some atmospheric conditions; if a non-absorbent flooring has been laid over it, then this may also assist with confirming the presence of magnesite. So, lifting a vinyl sheet floor covering and noting a heavy condensate would be very suggestive of this type of floor material.

Chapter 12
Joinery, doors and kitchens

Although everyone reading this book will probably have covered the properties of timber at college, it is amazing how often some of the basic principles are quickly forgotten, so the following points are certainly worth noting.

KEY CONSIDERATIONS

◆ **Timber moves – some of it moves a lot (usually, but not always, softwoods) – and although it is essentially dimensionally stable along its length, timber can move quite significantly across the grain and across its width.**

Even 'craftsmen' of yesteryear sometimes forgot this basic principle. Many timber defects (in older properties, but also in new) occur either as a result of errors in the original construction or because of subsequent unsympathetic repairs (for example, repairs which secure timber panels thus preventing them from moving and leading to shrinks, splits, warping and so on).
For all external joinery:

◆ **Consider why the defect was caused in the first place – drips, throats, hoods over windows, sealant mastic and so on all need to be examined carefully so that poorly designed details are not perpetuated.**

◆ **If necessary, carry out a careful condition survey to establish the condition of all of the windows or doors, and the extent of repairs required.**

◆ **When specifying components for a repair (or replacement) check some samples – incorrect detailing can increase the cost-in-use, to the point where the cost of maintenance and repair is considerably higher than any savings made initially.**

In many instances the repairs needed will be based on traditional joinery techniques. But some of the skills were lost during the latter part of the 20th century under the influence of 'modern methods of construction' and a shortage of skilled labour. Therefore:

◆ **Check that the building contractor or joiner fully understands what is required of them in terms of the quality of work and appropriate attention to detail.**

Given the shortage of skilled workers (or the long wait for those who do have the knowledge) it is tempting – whether you are dealing with one or two small isolated projects, or even when managing a substantial estate – to carry out wholesale replacement of defective components or fittings that are nearing the end of their serviceable life. After all, new components can be bought in bulk quite cheaply and the labour cost of fitting, say, 50 new front doors might appear quite attractive when compared with a repairs strategy.

However, I would suggest it is important to carefully consider repair before replacement, for the following reasons:

- Repair may offer a more ecologically sound solution than replacement.
- Even in some comparatively humble but old building stock many of the doors and windows may offer a design heritage, which is worth retaining and cannot be easily replicated by modern components.
- If you are willing to use modern repair methods (such as two-pack resins), then localised repairs can be carried out which could not be effected using traditional timber repair methods.

Defective sash windows are a good example. There are many sash windows still in existence (100 years old or more) but, given the method of construction, replacement of these windows can be an expensive option.

However, they are very much part of the British style of construction, and where these windows have been replaced either piecemeal or wholesale the whole aspect of a building's elevation can be dramatically altered. And if the building is Listed, the windows will comprise an integral element of that Listed status, so repair is essential.

Sash windows are relatively efficient in use and, though reasonably easy to repair, this can be time consuming (with associated labour costs – see box, right) and prone to rattling and draughts if the work is not done correctly. If your contractor does not have the necessary skills, you could consider a specialist repair company.

Finally, if you are carrying out refurbishment or alteration works, which are subject to 'the Regs', remember to check against the current Building Regulations or appropriate British Standards (for example, Part M of the Building Regulations, which relates to access to buildings; and Part B, on fire resistance – see Chapter 5). It is not always possible to make old components comply with modern Regulations, but it can sometimes be done.

Sash window repairs

A sash window with dimensions of about 2 m height by 1.5 m maximum width could cost up to £300 to repair, as the 'cost sequence' below shows. But once the repair is finished, the window might give another 100 years of service!

Sample cost sequence

1. Carefully remove sash beads and remove sliding sashes.
2. Break out sash box and disassemble pulley and weight mechanism.
3. Check and overhaul wedged tenons to sash frame and allow for localised punching in and re-tightening of wedges as required.
4. Replace sash cords. Clean off and lubricate sash pulleys.
5. Make allowance for cutting out of lower stiles to each side of window cill and scarfing in new timber to lower 300 mm section on outer of face of sash box.
6. Make allowance for two-pack resin repair to window cill over say 500 mm by maximum depth 30 mm. Bring forward to clean surface in line with original/existing cill timber.
7. Re-assemble sash weight pulley and cord and close sash box. Allow for new timber insert to close box. Lubricate siding sash sections with paraffin wax.
8. Bring forward all previously painted parts and allow for primer to new timber, 1 undercoat and 1 top coat. Leave to be readily opened, closed and secured and allow for fitting of new threaded sash lock bolt.

Total cost: £300 (assuming no special access provisions or scaffolding are required).

The box, Joinery – the basics, should serve as a useful aide memoire to timber and joinery issues when you are out on a site inspection.

JOINERY – THE BASICS

Timber quality

Much of the wood in use today is of comparatively low density when compared with some of the more slowly grown timbers of yesteryear. Consequently it may be prone to excess shrinkage than some of the more seasoned and densely grown timbers.

Timber is generally stress graded by looking at the density of the grain and counting the number of knots. There are machines available to do this. Some of them work better than others. The British Standards on visual strength grading methods were both updated in 2007: BS 4978: 2007, *Visual strength grading of softwood. Specification*, and BS 5756: 2007, *Visual stress grading of hardwood.*

There is a scheme of European 'CE' marking for timber components to verify their fitness for purpose, and the British Standards also set out a variety of guidance for the stress grading of timber and its performance standards.

There have been instances where the stress grading of timber for constructional purposes may not have been wholly reliable, and certainly it is comforting when you see a good tradesman examining material visually and rejecting anything not suitable for purpose.

Sustainability

Ideally, timber should be from a well-managed source. This is essential for some social housing schemes, for example, where the use of certified timber products will score better in environmental assessment schemes such as the Code for Sustainable Homes.

There are a number of timber certification schemes, the Forestry Stewardship Council (FSC) being one of the most well known (*www.fsc-uk.org*).

In general, timber components achieve higher environmental scores than, say, PVC products, which are manufactured from petrochemicals and are less easily recycled than timber-based components. (Although recycling of some plastics is possible, there is a carbon impact for that process too, over and above the original manufacturing.)

Timber 'substitutes'

Timber substitutes such as plywood, medium-density fibreboard (MDF) and chipboard offer some considerable advantages over timber. For example, they are all relatively dimensionally stable. This offers advantages in that shrinkage gaps are unlikely to appear around joints and details; MDF moulded door linings, architraves or skirting boards can be particularly successful in this regard. They are also quick and easy to fix and of course also do not require any 'knotting' or 'stopping', which can spoil the paintwork (if omitted) with a conventional timber.

These products can also be fairly cheap.

But there are some downsides. For example, standard grade chipboard is particularly prone to damage when wetted, and there are numerous failures under flat roof decks or in kitchen and bathroom floors. Where chipboard sheet is used, cutting out localised sections to replace damaged parts can be quite problematic.

There is also a question mark over the sustainability of these products. Composite materials such as MDF or chipboard can generate quite a low score in any environmental assessments due to: the problems with recycling this material at the end of its life; the amount of energy used up to create the material in the first place (the embodied energy); and the health and safety risks associated with their manufacture and during construction (from fine dust particles and release of formaldehyde). (A zero-formaldehyde MDF is available (Medite ZF), but it is imported from Germany and is more expensive.)

Woodwork glues

Over the last 20–30 years, use of 'two-pack' resin products has grown. These glues can deliver effective repairs at relatively low cost, where replacement of a whole window (or door, etc.) might otherwise be required.

There are various sorts of two-pack resins on the market, but all will have a 'pack' of resin and a 'pack' of catalyst (hardener) which is mixed in to cure the compound. Many of these incorporate some form of bulking agent within the resin, such as a powder or fibre compound. One or two companies, however, manufacture two-pack resin systems which incorporate 'neat' resin with no bulking agents. These offer a very effective repairs option because once bonded to sound timber (extremely careful eradication of all rotted components or softened timber is necessary) a very good adhesion can be obtained. The resin can be planed and shaped as if it were timber and is sufficiently plastic to accommodate movement due to thermal and moisture content changes.

You will notice that I mention the two-pack resin rather often in this chapter. (I do not hold shares in a resin factory, honest!) The reason is simple: these resins offer an extremely adaptable and effective method of carrying out repairs, which otherwise would require an expensive and highly skilled craftsperson, or perhaps would require wholesale replacement of large sections of window or door frame. However, they do need to be properly used; failure to correctly prepare surfaces for bonding will lead to a rapid failure of the repair.

PROBLEMS – JOINERY, DOORS AND KITCHENS

12.1 *MOISTURE DAMAGE TO TIMBER CLADDING*

One of the main problems you are likely to encounter is components dating from the 1960s, '70s and '80s, which are prone to decay due to moisture entrapment, which is, in turn, caused by poor detailing of the timber components originally. Often this means that items such as glazing beads have no bevelled edge or fall, to drain and discharge water away; water then sits on the flat timber surfaces or drains down into the end grain at joints, rapidly accelerating decay.

Correct detailing would have been fairly cheap and easy to do when the component was manufactured, and is presumably omitted either out of laziness or with a view to saving a few pennies at the point of manufacture.

Similar problems also arise in the modern 'Tudor-bethan' house with lots of plywood and stained softwood cladding; water will sit on any square edge it can find, with obvious consequences.

Solution 1

It may be possible to apply timber beads or quadrants to help drain water off the top edge – perhaps bedded in a clear mastic in order to seal the bead/joint and prevent moisture becoming entrapped behind.

Alternatively, the bead could be bedded in using two-pack polymer resin.

Solution 2

It may be possible to strike a bevel along the top edge of the timber. However, the tools required to strike a bevelled fall onto the square edges safely or conveniently are probably only owned by a high-class joiner, so this solution may not always be cost-effective.

Note also that wielding a high-speed router at height on a ladder is not recommended.

12.2 *MOISTURE INGRESS AT A BAY WINDOW*

The mitres around any bay windows are notorious sites for moisture ingress. The mitres shrink back, then water enters the open joint and causes decay at the end grain.

Solution 1

If you encounter the problem before significant decay has taken hold, a two-pack resin may be your salvation.

Solution 2

If decay is significant, it may be necessary to carefully split off any defective cills before installing new.

Traditionally this was achieved by fixing screws into the sound timber once the cill had split off, and drilling holes corresponding with the screw heads, in the new cill section. This was then set over the screw heads and hammered sideways so that the screws bit into the timber. However, this method does not guarantee a good joint/union between the new cill and the old timber, and water could soon enter the gap, causing further decay at great depth back into the cill or window frame section.

Again, use of two-pack resin buttered and pasted along the old timber frame to provide a good seal is probably a more efficient and effective solution.

The mitres will always present a problem, however, and it may be best to cut back the mitre slightly and provide a substantial filling of resin rather than try to paint-fill a hairline crack, which will inevitably open up and allow water penetration sooner or later.

Ugly but effective

I have sometimes seen repairs incorporating lead flashing dressed down over the mitred corners. This is sometimes quite an effective short to medium term repair, although it is an extremely ugly solution to the problem.

12.3 STILES AND MULLIONS

The bottom sections of stiles/mullions – that is, the vertical timbers supporting the window frame – are also a classic weak point for water penetration. Rainwater, particularly on a south or western aspect, is driven into the joint, sucked up into the end grain and decays both the cill and the bottom of the stile or mullion.

Solution

Repairs in this situation can be quite difficult, although it is sometimes possible for a good tradesman to cut out the bottom section of the mullion and let in a new section of sound timber. These are, of course, always prone to further rot if moisture either becomes trapped behind the repair or enters along the line of the scarfed joint.

> **Remember, if done properly the scarfed section should have a joint sloping so that the lower edge of the repair is on the outside face of the timber. But just as frequently it is done the other way round, which is prone to trapping moisture, or the repair falls out because it is not properly dovetailed and locked into place (see diagram, right).**

Bedding the new sound timber within a two-pack resin base can offer an extremely sound repair and extend the life of the components considerably.

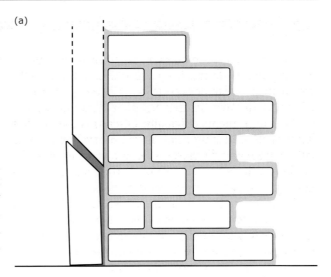

(a)

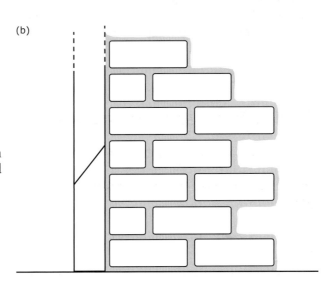

(b)

Scarfed timber repairs. (a) This way is not uncommon! (b) Scarfed in this way the timber post is retained in position.

12.4 OVERHAULING BROKEN JOINTS

Modern components tend to be framed up using dowelled joints. Although this produces a fitting that appears the same as a properly mortice and tenoned construction – to start with – the problem is that this technique often allows the timber to 'cup' and warp and distort, particularly if any water enters the end grain of the joint. The dowelled joint is inherently weaker than a tenoned one, so early water ingress leads to accelerated distortion of the timber ... leading to more water ingress, and thus to early breakdown of the joint (unless it is very well maintained or in a sheltered location).

Doors and windows that are properly tenoned together with through-joints are likely to have a considerably extended life, improved cost-in-use and are more easily repaired.

It is sometimes possible to repair this kind of defect, but it usually requires (in the case of a door) removing the door entirely and boring through the frame to insert new substantial dowelled pegs from one side of the frame (stile) into the rail to lock the timbers in position.

If a doorframe of this sort fails there are several options. The first two techniques described overleaf assume that you have access to a well-trained craftsperson.

> **Note that these techniques can be applied to sash windows as well as doors and other window types.**

Solution 1

If the door is of any age, consider completely removing it, breaking all the joints open, reassembling them and re-gluing them.

If the door is quite old it is possible the original glue was an animal glue, which is prone to breaking down with age, moisture ingress and so on. Modern glues such as polyvinyl acetate (PVA) offer considerable adhesion compared with the traditional alternatives, but nevertheless these are still prone to deterioration if there is any moisture ingress.

Careful external decoration normally overcomes this, but use of waterproof glues such as urea-formaldehyde glue (e.g. ResinMite, formerly known as Cascamite) will offer a long-lasting alternative.

Note that it would not be possible to deconstruct the door in the future if further repairs were required.

Because of their permanence, waterproof glues may not be appropriate in conservation work.

Solution 2

A second option would be to apply cramps to the door in order to straighten it up prior to repinning some of the joints and tightening wedges into the tenons, but without actually completely deconstructing the door.

Solution 3

A third alternative would be to apply localised scarfed-in timber repairs if the frame or door will stand it, or to use a two-pack resin, as outlined above.

Use of resins, of course, assumes the door would be stained or painted.

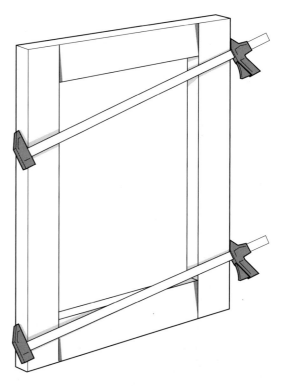

Re-gluing the frame using carefully positioned cramps to help re-align and 'square up'.

12.5 DOORS DROPPING AND BROKEN JOINTS

This is a common problem in older properties, as the old animal glues fail and 100 years or more of wear and tear takes it toll.

Solution

It should be reasonably straightforward to loosen the wedges securing the tenons into the doorframe rails, and break the door apart. The framework does not always require total dismantling.

Injecting with a new PVA joinery glue and re-cramping the doorframe with new wedges should enable it to be pulled back into square.

If necessary, some new lipping pieces can be added to square-up, if the door has been previously planed away to fit the opening as it has started to sag.

● Assuming a painted finish is applied, then the repairs should be virtually invisible.
● Bedding in new timber strips in two-pack epoxy glues can provide a virtually seamless finish.

COST SEQUENCE – Repairs to traditional mortice and tenon rail construction panel door

1. Remove door from frame by un-screwing hinges from frame. Allow for temporary closure of the door opening.
2. Carefully chisel out or tap out wedges securing tenon ends.
3. Break apart stiles and rails. Mark all positions for re-assembly.
4. Remove fielded panels. Clean off all edges and paint build up where panels locate in grooves in frame. Mark positions and set aside for re-assembly.
5. Clean off all loose material dirt and dust from joints. Check tightness of fit.
6. Cut new wedges, sized to fit adjusted slots in tenon ends.
7. Re-assemble door. Allow for use of limited PVA glue (water soluble providing some scope for disassembly for the future). Close up all joints with cramps and secure with wedges to tenons. Adjust door to ensure it is square to opening using cramp positioning.
8. Allow for two-pack resin gluing-in of fillet to head or base of door where any wear has occurred on one top or bottom rail only. Flush in to door timbers.
9. Bring forward and redecorate 1 primer, 2 undercoat and 1 topcoat.

Repairs to traditional mortice and tenon rail construction panel door – COST £160

12.6 STAIRS WITH INADEQUATE STRINGS

Old staircases probably generate more repair problems than any other internal feature.

In cheaper work the sloping boards running alongside the stairs to support the treads and risers – the strings or stringboards – can be of extremely thin timber. Consequently the housing joints cut to receive the treads and risers of the stairs may have very little purchase. If the staircase is fixed to a main wall on one side only, the other side of the stair is subject to significant leverage action which, over time, can lever out the treads and risers from their joints.

This can generate one of the most difficult repairs scenarios: can the stairs be repaired? Or is complete replacement of some or all of the staircase necessary?

Given that much of the housing joint is likely to have worn away with a century or more of use, it is unlikely that the original joint can be reinstated by jacking the stairs back up into position.

Solution 1

Assuming the strings are sound, it is very often possible to carry out effective repairs provided they are sympathetically done.

As soon as the stairs start to sag or treads spring, the first recourse of many temporary repairers is to put a few screws through the nosing of the stair into the riser to tighten up the whole construction.

This could have consequences for the condition of the nosings, however (see Problem 12.7 Nosing defects/flexing across riser).

Solution 2

If the strings are weak, but the staircase can be propped – safely – on its outer edge string, then it may be possible to reconstruct a suitable frame including sections of plywood cut into the underside of the housing to brace the joint.

The likelihood is, however, that the expense of making a good job of this detail (and the risk of future movement) means that a whole new flight of stairs needs to be let in.

Solution 3

If that is the case, it is not always necessary to replace the entire staircase – the section could be pre-fabricated and let into place.

However, this can cause other problems:

● The Building Owner will not be able to use the upper floor while the works are in progress.
● It can be extremely difficult to physically get a flight of stairs into the building without causing damage to decorations.

The defect often occurs in flats where they have been converted from a much larger building. In this situation, a considerable number of owners might be affected by the access issue and a temporary access might need to be installed or works carried out while some of the Building Owners are in temporary accommodation. All of which can have an extremely adverse affect on the service charge at the end of the day for other Building Owners!

COST SEQUENCE – Defective strings to old staircase

1. Provide any temporary support to the staircase as necessary.
2. Break out defective wedges to housing joints under the staircase.
3. Glue and screw new plywood reinforcing plates to underside face of string to provide new/reinforced housing for the wedges. Use plates of 25-mm thick ply.
4. Cut new wedges and drive back into new houses when glue has set to the reinforcing plates.
5. Allow for, say, 12 plywood plate repairs and wedge sets.

6. Break out loose missing/defective rubbed blocks to underside internal angle of stair tread and riser. Scrape off and clean away glue residue to leave timber faces in clean condition. Rub in and lightly tack or screw into place new soft wood blocks to internal angle. Use PVA glue. Nominal minimum timber size, say, 40-mm square section.

Staircases – defective strings to old staircase – COST £110

12.7 NOSING DEFECTS/FLEXING ACROSS RISER

Repair work may cause the nosing to break off the stair (see 12.6 Solution 1, above), and because only localised bracing is in place, further sagging usually occurs sooner or later. It should be easy to splice on the nosing by the glue-and-screw method for minor damage, but if the damage is worse, a more comprehensive repair (below) is a better bet.

Solution 1

It is fairly easy to carry out a proper repair, but it usually involves installing new glued 'rubbed' blocks under the tread and riser junction and to either tighten up the existing wedges under the stairs or insert new ones (traditional staircase constructions were made to permit this).

How the 'rubbed blocks' got their name
The rubbed blocks are so-called because small triangles of timber were literally rubbed into place using an animal glue, which would set very quickly, and provide localised stiffening to the joint of the tread and riser. (The old glues were melted and would cool – and set – quite rapidly.)

New blocks can be put into place and fixed temporarily with screws or light nails while the glue sets. Use of a modern PVA glue would be appropriate, and the blocks need to be tight-fitting to prevent flexing at the joint; though the setting times are somewhat extended compared with a thermosetting material (i.e. traditional animal glue).

The timber must be clean to ensure a good glue adhesion.

Solution 2

Alternatively, if they are obviously loose, then careful tightening of the wedges will effect more improvement than anything. If it looks as though the wedges may drop out they can be glued into place and temporarily held with a masonry nail or similar.

Pre-repair checks:

- Have any of the lower treads or the newel post rotted away due to either ongoing or previous damp? Any collapse or settling in that area (e.g. due to softened timber) will inherently distort the stairs and, if it does not reach a state of equilibrium, the distortion will cause ongoing further deterioration to the construction. Again, folding wedges can be used to lift the construction from behind/beneath, although it might be necessary to plate around the bottom of the structure with some plywood to cosmetically mask the propping up carried out.
- Are the stairs bearing on a solid foundation? Although a little unusual, it is certainly not unheard of for the stairs to be constructed off the floorboards (which may well 'miss' the joists at this point) or even off a brick sleeper wall at the ground floor – any or all of which may have sunk, decayed, deteriorated or never existed in the first place. And all carefully hidden by a thick layer of carpet! In this instance, fabrication of some joists or bearings of suitably robust size timbers fixed across the sleeper walls – rather like nogging pieces – will be necessary before carrying out any other works to repair the stairs.

COST SEQUENCE – Staircase nosing repairs

1. Assumes a 16-riser staircase.
2. Carefully split out nosings to existing staircase. Allow for creating a new true edge by setting timber circular saw to appropriate depth of tread and cut in through the main nosing. Ensure the cut is positioned so that it does not interrupt the housing joint for the riser slotted into the tread.
3. Glue and screw into place new nosing with bull nosed moulding to leading edge. Set in two-pack resin to provide adequate filling to the joint between old and new.
4. Allow for careful flushing off of the joint on completion to leave in clean and sound condition and securely bonded.

Staircase nosing repairs – COST £185

12.8 NEWEL POST/RAILS CUT AWAY

Another common defect encountered in refurbishment projects is where an older property was 'improved' during the 1960s – the newel posts and handrails were sawn away to create an open aspect staircase.

This does not comply with either the British Standard or Building Regulations in terms of trip hazard, fall hazard or handrail support.

Some 75% of falls in domestic properties occur on staircases. and on any section of a staircase where there is no handrail. This predominantly affects children and the elderly.

Solution

Robust hand-railing (rather than a cosmetic but ineffective baluster) is an important requirement and should always be reinstated.

COST SEQUENCE – Repairs to hand railing/newel posts and balustrade to staircase

1. Assumes no more than say 16 risers in a flight to be repaired.
2. Trim and prepare surface to any broken or cut away newel posts to provide a flat position to locate new timber.
3. Bore a hole through centre of original/in situ newel post, sufficient to receive, e.g., M20 stud bolt. Cut slot in side of newel post to receive nut.
4. Insert nut and thread in stud bolt. Cut newel post to adequate height to receive handrail/balustrade, and cut slot at side to receive nut with sufficient room for spanner to turn. Thread new newel post minimum section size say 100 mm by 100 mm over stud bolt and tighten.
5. Ensure that newel post is rigidly fixed with no play.
6. Cut in mortice to receive handrail tenon.
7. Set moulded beads to receive balustrade base sections. Measure and space centres for balustrade fixing and cut infill blocking pieces to sit between mouldings to suit centres.
8. Secret nail or tack nail alternately blocking pieces and baluster to locate on stair string and locate within chase within the handrail.
9. Secure all fixing points.
10. Sand down and bring forward ready to receive decorations.

Repairs to handrailing/newel posts and balustrade to staircase – COST £125

12.9 LADDER-EFFECT BALUSTERS

In properties of the 1960s and 1970s, horizontal rail enclosures were frequently installed, but these are equally likely to offer a beautiful set of rungs for children to climb along – with the risk that they may descend head-first down the stairs if they manage to make it over.

Solution

Replacement with a vertical baluster or full enclosure is much to be preferred.

If need be, this can be on a temporary basis using ply over-sheeting across the face of the balusters or a similar arrangement.

If the newel posts are missing but the remainder of the stairs are sound, it should be possible to reinstate a newel post by driving in engineering stud threads before screwing on a new newel post section. A couple of ways of achieving this are shown below.

Once newel posts have been secured, it should be possible to fit a new handrail and baluster enclosure.

Remember to refer to the Building Regulations: the balusters should be at 100-mm centres to prevent small heads from being wedged through.

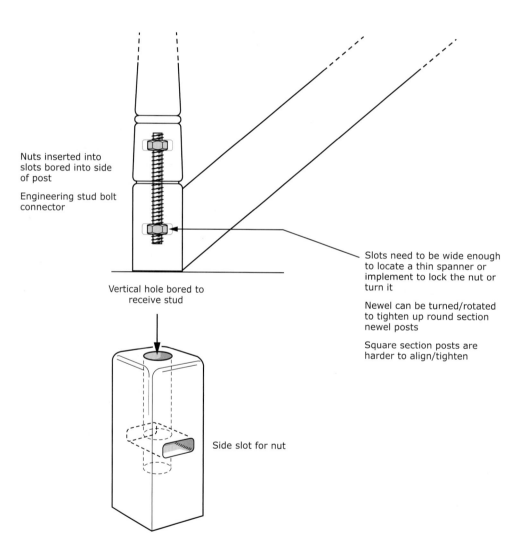

Nuts inserted into slots bored into side of post

Engineering stud bolt connector

Vertical hole bored to receive stud

Slots need to be wide enough to locate a thin spanner or implement to lock the nut or turn it

Newel can be turned/rotated to tighten up round section newel posts

Square section posts are harder to align/tighten

Side slot for nut

Repair to cut down newel post.

12.10 SPLIT PANELS (DOORS)

This frequently occurs – very often because the paintwork applied around the door's beads or panels effectively glued the edges of the panel into the frame, preventing it from moving across the grain with changes in temperature and humidity.

Solution 1

One option is to carefully tap in a slightly tapered fillet of timber and planing it flush with the original panel. A neat finish can be achieved if glue is used to secure it (or possibly use an epoxy two-pack to fill in any gaps which were missed due to an irregular split).

Use of a side rebate plane – a reasonably specialist joiner's tool – or modern electrical router run along a bead can be used to straighten up any uneven splits so that timber fillets can be inserted neatly.

Solution 2

In severe cases, where timber beads have been applied around the field or opening to secure the panels instead of using a moulding cut into the door itself, it may be necessary to split out the beads, re-cramp the panel which has split, then glue the edges back together before supplying new beads to re-secure it (unless the old beads can be very carefully salvaged).

Modern routers can create a variety of moulded finishes, so it should be possible to closely replicate the original in most cases.

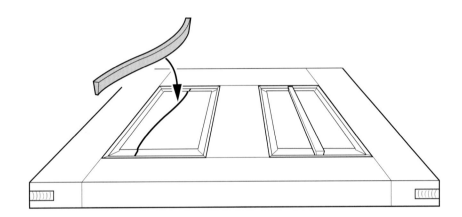

Crack in panel cut open. Fillet or veneer tapped in.
Secured in two-pack resin glue which acts as filler, or
PVA if a good fit with no large gaps

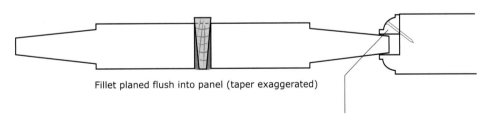

Fillet planed flush into panel (taper exaggerated)

May be able to break out the bead
if it is glued and not moulded in
solid timber in the door rail

COST SEQUENCE – Repair to split panel of fielded panel timber door

1. Repair assumes a single panel is being repaired over a maximum length of 1 m. The panels are assumed to be fielded/have bevelled edges inserted into the frame.
2. Carefully rake out split to panel using electrical router or splitting tool to multi-plane to provide straight edges to the split.
3. Prepare timber fillet to match the opening width. Slightly taper fillet in section.
4. Insert fillet to crack and tap into place setting in PVA glue.
5. Flush timber fillet to face of panel and across a fielded bevel.
6. Bring forward panel surface and allow for 1 primer, 2 undercoats and 1 top coat to match original finish.

Repair to split panel of fielded panel timber door – COST £145

12.11 FILLING OLD HOLES

Old doors and windows will often include holes which once housed locks and so on.

Solution

Careful cutting out the area using a plug-cutting tool on an electric drill should enable any smaller holes such as screw holes to be plugged with new timber.

This provides an almost invisible repair if carefully done i.e. the timber is reasonably well matched in the direction of the grain and is then planed flush prior to refinishing.

There used to be a tool available for use with a joiner's bit brace; it would cut a beautifully tapered plug that could be tapped into place and the grain matched up and aligned. But I have not seen these for some years. If carrying out work on better quality premises it may be worth checking with the building contractor's joiner to see if they have some such thing available or could use other tools to make an invisible 'patch'.

12.12 UPGRADING FIRE RESISTANCE

In order to ensure that the building has adequate fire protection you will need to refer to the most recent version of the Building Regulations Approved Document B (2007). (Indeed, the Building Regulations have changed so rapidly over the past five years that it is advisable to keep abreast of developments – Chapter 5 gives the full list of Building Regulations at the end of 2007.)

- In particular, the 'old' rules about fitting fire closers to doors – especially on houses above 4.5 metres in height (i.e. those with a second floor) – have relaxed somewhat. However, there is still a need to fit a closer to a door that communicates with a garage.
- Flats must have closers fitted to the main entrance doors and around common parts.
- There are now separate, more complex, requirements for houses in multiple occupation (HMOs).

In summary, check before you act.

Solutions 2 and 3 will help preserve the original finishes and mouldings to the door fabric.

Solution 1

Panelled doors can be uprated where fire resistance needs to be improved.

This usually requires the removal of the beads securing the door panels so that the panels (if flush) can be resurfaced with a fire resistant material and beads refixed.

Solution 2

Where the panels have been moulded so that the edges taper into the groove in the frame then it may be necessary to saw a kerf (a groove) into the panel so that a fire-resistant panel (or sometimes paste material) can be inserted within the thickness of the panel.

Considerable care is needed when cutting the kerf. This requires use of a good panel or radial saw to accurately cut in.

Although this is a specialist process, and unlikely to be used often, it is something to be aware of and retain in your mental armoury of options. Obviously this is a rather more expensive option, but it is worth considering where historic or high-quality buildings are involved.

Solution 3

One system also used as an intumescent paste inserted into the thickness of the panel through the saw kerf.

COST SEQUENCE – Upgrading fire resistance to panel doors

1. Remove door. Carefully cut out any wedges to tenons and break apart door rails and stiles.
2. Carefully remove panels from fielding grooves.
3. Set circular saw or high quality bandsaw to align with edge of panel and slice panel through centre.
4. Construct sandwich with intumescent board set in centre of panel. Glue all surfaces and clamp together to construct new panel with sandwiched fire lining in centre. Use fire-resisting/fire-rated non-flammable and non-melt glue.
5. When all panels complete reassemble door with intumescent lining set to centre of fielded panel.
6. Reassemble door and re-wedge all tenon joints. Glue and cramp and check door fits original opening.
7. Bring forward, 1 primer 2 undercoat, and finishing coat of paint.

Upgrading fire resistance to panel doors – COST £300

12.13 HANGING DOORS – GENERAL

When hanging doors, there seems to be considerable temptation for less-skilled onsite labour to simply plane off the edges of a door which does not fit cleanly using a rather drastic approach – planing the door across the width of the edge.

Solution

The correct technique is to plane the door at a bevel, so that a neat edge is maintained at the door opening. The sketch explains this.

Likewise when fitting new linings it is important that the mouldings are fitted one to the other.

- It is pointless cutting moulded architraves or linings to go on a door surround within a mitre box to ensure a perfect 45-degree fit if in fact the opening is not perfectly at right angles. In this instance the usual practice is to cut one section at exactly 45 degrees and scribe over the second timber piece held over its final position on the door lining to ensure a perfect fit at whatever slight mismatched angle might be required.

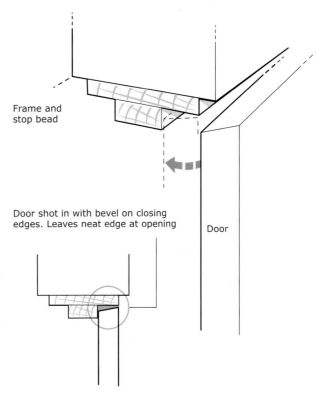

Frame and stop bead

Door shot in with bevel on closing edges. Leaves neat edge at opening

Door

Chapter 13
Flues, fireplaces and chimneys

Flues, fireplaces and chimneys are common areas where repairs or more radical treatments are required. Hidden defects can rapidly eat into the budget for refurbishment works, causing considerable distress to owners, occupiers or developers who have only a limited budget to deal with these things.

So bear in mind that whatever you are faced with, it is probably well worth spending an extra ten minutes of investigation time to check the overall structure of the chimney.

KEY CONSIDERATIONS

With pressure on space particularly impacting on smaller old properties – typically the two-bed terraced house – it is not uncommon to find that many of the chimney breasts have been removed.

- ◆ **This may leave inadequately supported chimney masonry on upper floors, within the roof space and above the roofline of course.**

If the works have been carried out properly, then you should find substantial support – hopefully some form of steel joist, although sometimes timber is used. If the timber is of sufficient dimension then all is well and good, but this is not always the case. I have often found chimney breasts supported (perhaps in the roof space), on nothing more than the ceiling joists or a few pieces of 'four-by-two' softwood.

- ● The problem is not always apparent from casual inspection, and on a refurbishment project it is well worth walking round the property carrying out a simple sketch plan of each floor to establish if chimney breasts appear in some positions but not at the corresponding level on another floor.

- ● An inspection of the roof space is also required, and sometimes there can still be a ton of masonry supported within the roof space but removed from above the roofline and beneath the top floor ceiling joists.

- ◆ **However, it's also possible that the opposite may be true: the formation of a chimney, flue and hearth may have effectively created a section of wall that is better supported than the lightweight foundations on the remainder of it. This can be a cause of differential settlement in the wall, and so it is worth bearing this in mind when inspecting to carry out repairs to other parts of the structure.**

As with all other building elements, it is wise to pay careful attention to what has caused the problem you are attempting to fix. For example, when assessing distortion to the chimney, consider whether water may be penetrating and exacerbating the problem. (Frequently the cement flaunching smoothed around at the top of the stack to drain water away has cracked, allowing water to actually penetrate into the masonry. So, checking and repair of the flaunching condition is one of the first things to establish, and may well require a long ladder inspection.)

The box overleaf should serve as a useful aide memoire when you are out on a site inspection.

CHIMNEYS – THE BASICS

Flue design

For many years chimneys were designed with a fairly straight flue profile, particularly so for provincial properties.

But from the Georgian period onwards flues became rather more convoluted as they twisted their way up the building. This makes repairs and maintenance considerably more difficult.

The modern trend for restricted-draught fires (whether of the radiant gas fire or wood or solid fuel burning type) means that higher flue and gas temperatures are achieved than these fireplaces were ever designed for, and careful consideration therefore needs to be given to maintenance and repair strategy.

A sheet metal cap over old chimney pots – no ventilation is apparent.

Sulfate attack

Sulfates that were present in the flue gases of coal fires or traditional coal–gas gas fires are deposited on the inside of the chimney. In the presence of moisture (i.e. condensation), the sulfates react with tri-calcium aluminate (present in Portland cement), and the sulfates expand, damaging brickwork and causing mortar to disintegrate.

This type of damage is difficult to see externally, but may sometimes cause horizontal cracks on the inner face of the wall (because it is under tension). If different types of brick have been used on the inner and outer faces of the chimney, bowing may occur.

Weathering of chimneys

A more obvious failure of traditional masonry chimneys is when they distort and bend out of plumb due to 'preferential wetting' – that is to say, under the influence of the prevailing wind and rain the chimney bends towards the south west.

This distortion is exacerbated by sulfation: migration of the brick and mortar joints caused by the presence of sulfates causes the masonry to expand and contract, gradually working its way towards the direction of the prevailing rain. Eventually this can significantly destabilise the chimney, requiring substantial structural repairs or replacement.

How much distortion is too much? The BRE's Good Building Guide 2 (May 1990) (*www.brebookshop.com*) suggests that about 1:100 deviation from plumb for a slender chimney stack would be about right, rather than the usual 'rule of thirds' distortion.

However, many chimney stacks on smaller terraced houses are comparatively stumpy and unlikely to show such elevated degrees of distortion.

PROBLEMS – FLUES, FIREPLACES AND CHIMNEYS

13.1 CRACKS TO CHIMNEYS

Distortion – including that caused by sulfation – can be so severe that the chimney will need to be carefully taken down and rebuilt.

> **If the building is Listed or in a conservation area, then not only will Listed Building Permission be required but careful reconstruction on a like-for-like basis will be essential.**

Many older chimneys do not incorporate either any damp proof material at all (such as a tray or adequate flashings) or if they do then often the detailing is inadequate or semi-functional. This could easily be improved upon by incorporating a proper sheet lead tray through the complete thickness of the stack together with properly fixed in flashings:

● Even on repair works this is frequently omitted, and contractors effectively replace the defective masonry like-for-like, missing the perfect opportunity to improve performance to moisture resistance.
● While the chimney is down, it may also provide the opportunity to improve the flue lining as well (see below).

Where repairs will suffice, however, a number of options are available.

Solution 1

Frequently the chimney fissures vertically as the masonry separating the flues expands, partly under the influence of contaminative sulfates.

If the fissuring is comparatively slight it may be possible to stitch back the masonry either:

● using twisted helical bars (see Chapter 9, problem 9.17); or
● by putting a belt around the chimney at intervals of courses.

The latter involves winding stainless steel or copper wire through the mortar courses which have been cut back and are then face pointed. This effectively puts a simple truss or corset around the chimney to restrain future movement.

> **When carrying out re-pointing repairs it is important to ensure that moisture entrapment is not made worse – so the use of rich modern Portland cement mortars in older chimneys that had lime mortar joints would not be appropriate; a breathable lime mortar would be the ideal option.**

Where it is possible to use a Portland cement mortar it would be appropriate to use a sulfate-resistant specification rather than a conventional Portland cement straight out of the bag.

Where frost damage and erosion has affected the brick, again possibly coupled with chemical attack, then, given care, it should be possible to carefully cut out and let in new bricks.

If the degree of cracking through the chimney is too bad it may be possible to carefully let in new bricks, stitching across the crack, although some of the mortar joints at the perpends will necessarily be rather thicker than in the original work.

It may be tempting to render the chimney, but again issues of sulfate-resistant mortars have to be considered.

Where render is used it is important to use properly gauged coats in accordance with the British Standards (see Problem 9.15). And if there is any risk of the chimney cracking or much moisture penetrating (in a severely exposed position for example) rendering may have the effect of trapping more moisture within the masonry. Hairline cracks would soon develop under exposed conditions, and after a couple of years the chimney is likely to be in a very sorry state.

13.2 CONDENSATION

Older chimneys can be particularly prone to condensation – especially where the flue is buttressed on an outside wall.

If the chimney is flush with the flank wall of a house, it is possible that it is only half a brick thick. This allows moisture to penetrate, causing localised cooling in the flue, and thus increasing the risk of condensation together with general air/surface cooling

of the masonry, particularly at higher levels of the wall, where air movement is likely to be more pronounced.

Short of adding another skin to the wall, weather protection may be extremely hard to achieve and for many terraced houses, which have 100 per cent site coverage, there is unlikely to be scope to build out beyond the boundary.

Risk of chimney fires

Originally many of the chimneys/flues would have been lined with render smoothed up the inside of the flue. With age, the render will have deteriorated, and frequently the flues are found to comprise soft powdery eroded brick when they are broken open for examination. This can lead to a number of problems, in addition to condensation.

As the mortar courses deteriorate, ledges can form which might encourage burning soot to build up.

Additionally, in older properties, it is not uncommon for the odd joist to have been built into the masonry of the flue/chimney breast, and as the parging cement lining deteriorates from the flue the ends of some timbers can become exposed.

If the fireplace continues in use, then first charring and then eventually a chimney fire is a possibility.

Another risk factor arises when fireplaces are to be brought back into use with restricted-draught fires such as enclosed wood burning stoves, Parkray™-style solid fuel stoves, and the like. Then, a lining is particularly important:

> **Modern fires have very high flue gas temperatures which can aggressively attack masonry chimneys. The presence of a flue lining not only protects the masonry, it helps the chimney to draw, by creating an insulated lining which heats up causing convection to draw flue gases efficiently through the height of the flue and chimney.**

Solution 1

A number of proprietary systems are available to re-line the flues, including the one method, which uses a cast steel ball drawn up the chimney to force cement dropped above it into a circular profile and line the flue accordingly.

Solution 2

Another option is to break open sections of the chimney breast and flue to insert ceramic liners.

Solution 3

Stainless steel flexible lining pipes offer an extremely efficient option to line the flue. However, this is likely to be practicable only where there are very few bends, kinks or distortions within the line of the flue. If that is the case, you will need to revert to Solution 2.

- If the flue liner is, in turn, insulated on its outer face by sand or mica its efficiency can again be improved and the masonry insulated from any flue gas or contamination. The material can be poured to fill the gap between the liner and the chimney.

Solution 4

A compromise method of strengthening a damaged chimney which is badly eroded on the inside face is described in *Chimneys in old buildings* (SPAB Technical Pamphlet 3, by GBA Williams; though sadly now out of print since the reprinted third edition in 1990, if you cannot purloin a copy from a colleague, it is listed on the IHSTI subscription website) – a document I highly recommend. (It also describes methods of mitigating or curing smoking chimneys by adjusting the hearth and fireback positions.)

The method uses a stainless steel mesh or grill within the chimney, new flue lining pots inserted from above, and fill with a render or grout to strengthen the hole.

COST SEQUENCE – Flue lining

1. Assumes chimney height of 1.3 m above ridgeline and typical 2-storey building. Floor-to-ceiling heights assumed 2.4 m.
2. For ground floor fireplace, install flexible steel flue lining taken to secured terminal fitting at top of chimney and fixed to register plate above fireplace opening.
3. Assumes that no breaking out of the main chimney flue is required, and the flue liner can be inserted from ridge/roof level.
4. Pricing to allow for all necessary scaffold access to roof.
5. Make cost allowance for re-construction of, say, one quarter of the chimney stack and for cleaning and removal of soot from the flue prior to commencement of work.

Chimney flue lining – COST £935 (reusing existing pot); COST £1100 (new pot)

13.3 UNSUPPORTED CHIMNEY STACKS

A number of options are available and depend very much upon the individual circumstances in the property, so generalisation only is possible.

Solution 1

If the chimney is a structure built against the Party Wall in a semi-detached or terraced house, then with a bit of luck it should be possible to install a steel joist to pick up the load – supporting the joist in turn across internal load-bearing walls (or, sometimes, the front and rear main walls of the building when a substantial joist section may become necessary).

Bear in mind that it may be necessary to put in place a Party Wall Award if the RSJ needs to rest into the Party Wall (and thus changing its loading characteristics).

The RSJ will only sit beneath a portion of the chimney, so it is important to ensure that all the masonry is properly tied in and it would be suitable to support the upper section of the chimney stack on a reinforced concrete lintel (or more, if a large chimney).

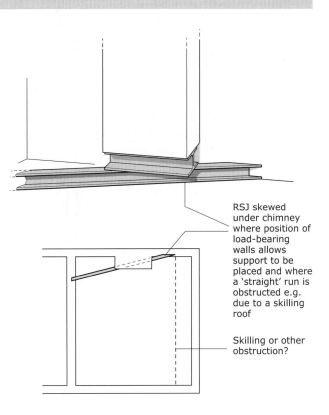

RSJ skewed under chimney where position of load-bearing walls allows support to be placed and where a 'straight' run is obstructed e.g. due to a skilling roof

Skilling or other obstruction?

The use of stainless steel helical bars to reinforce the joints of the upper sections of the chimney may be appropriate and help prevent its sagging or distorting and ensure the load is concentrated on the steel joists.

Sometimes it is possible to insert the RSJ running at an angle across the building if that is the only way in which lead bearing walls can be picked up (see diagram above, right).

If you are at all concerned that there is any significant additional load onto previously unloaded walls, then some checking of the wall's condition (the masonry bond) and the foundation bearing beneath the floors would be appropriate.

Certainly you need to ensure that the wall is continuous. For example, in a terraced house check that the wall has not been opened up between the lounge and dining room, changing the load path down to the ground floor.

Solution 2

The final option is to remove the chimney entirely and reinstate the roof and roof covering above if a suitable position for load-bearing components beneath cannot be located.

Chimneys on Listed Buildings

Total removal of a chimney may be a problem within a conservation area or with a Listed Building.

In these circumstances it is sometimes possible to obtain permission from the local authority to use a fibre-glass mock-up chimney to replace the masonry original.

If the alternative, i.e. leaving the defective structure in situ, would cause 'damage to the detriment of the character of a Listed Building', then it should be possible to persuade the local conservation officer accordingly. If in doubt it would be worth re-reading the Act in order to negotiate!

COST SEQUENCE – Take down chimney; 2-storey dwelling

1. Supply a scaffold tower access or scaffolding and roof ladder. Dust sheets to be placed within roof void to collect all light debris and dust.
2. Reduce 4-flue brick chimney by 2 m to below roof/rafter height.
3. Install new rafters inside of original trimming pieces to newly inserted ridge board in line with existing ridge.
4. Allow for additional timber/plywood plating over joints to secure all connections between old and new work (ridge board) and timber joist plating, where appropriate, around trimmers to secure new inserted rafter sections. Allow for good quality shear resistant stainless steel screw fixings with minimum 3 fixings on each side of each joint; alternatively, bolt through (allow for, say, total 6 no. fixings in engineering stud bolt per rafter plate about M12 diameter/thread).
5. Strip back margins of tile covering and lay in new roofing felt across the void with minimum 150 mm laps across rafter joints.
6. Install new hanging battens to match existing tile or slate gauge.
7. Fit new tiles (slates). Allow for stripping off rear elevation to match old tiles into the front elevation and hang new tiles on the exposed and stripped rear elevation sections.
8. Allow for cart away of all risings and clean the roof space of all debris. Strike the scaffold and clean away.

Take down chimney; 2-storey dwelling – COST £2700

Chapter 14
Drainage

The requirements for modern drainage systems are contained in Building Regulations (Approved Document H) – but of course this only deals with new work.

The Regulations now include advice for grey water recycling and 'reclaimed water systems' and for underground water storage (Approved Document H2).

The Regulations are well set out, so I do not propose to cover in great depth what is available, suffice to say that Approved Document Part H Building Regulations covers:

- sanitary pipework
- foul drainage
- adoption of sewers and connection to public sewers
- waste water treatment systems and cesspools and their maintenance
- rainwater drainage (touched on above under gutters and roofs)
- surface water drainage generally
- storage of solid waste
- water recycling.

The situation becomes a little more complicated, however, when carrying out repairs to existing buildings or extending or adding to existing structures and combining new and old systems. This is touched on in Appendix H1-B of Approved Document H.

Although the Building Regulations do not have specific requirements relating to maintenance and repair of drains and sewers, local authorities or the statutory authority (Statutory Undertaker) providing sewerage services do, however, have powers to ensure that appropriate maintenance is carried out and that repairs or alterations are properly executed.

This includes the power under Section 48 of The Public Health Act 1936 for the local authority to test drains or sewers if they suspect these are causing a health hazard.

So, although the Building Regulations do not necessarily apply directly to repairs and alterations of existing drain systems nevertheless it is only sensible to carry out the works in accordance with Approved Document H1. (The Regulations do, of course, apply as soon as you are carrying out works which constitute a 'building operation' as defined in the Building Act.) Upgrading substantial older drainpipe runs to modern performance standards, however, can be nigh on impossible. It is therefore sensible to consider an appropriate standard to assess these problems.

KEY CONSIDERATIONS

◆ **'Out of sight is out of mind' is not a good motto when it comes to underground drainage. You need to take an entirely opposite view, and ensure that the drainage system is thoroughly checked before you plan building or repair works. For starters, the drains may not be where you think they are!**

Sewers are not always where you think they are
It is not unheard of for building works to be suspended while an application has to be made for a sewer diversion. It may even be necessary to re-think the position of an extension or a main structural wall to move it away from a sewer line which has only been discovered once works have begun.

Sometimes even plotting the position of the drain between two chambers is not enough, and the supposed straight line between the two chamber positions may not exist despite whatever the Building Regulations and Best Practice would normally dictate!

If you do not take the sensible precaution of locating the actual position of drain runs you may end up with a considerable extra burden on cost and time once works have started. Even if you obtain drainage plans from the statutory authority (which it normally has to do free of charge), these may only prove indicative rather than give specific drain positions.

A Building Over Agreement may be necessary, and depending on the size and location of the drains this may only be possible at the discretion of the local authority (which sometimes acts as agent on behalf of the statutory sewerage authority) or you may need to make an application to the statutory services provider. Permission is not guaranteed.

Depending on the policy of the sewerage provider this could be a very expensive operation. I recently encountered one sewerage authority that charged in the region of £10,000 for *any* sewer diversion!

Your client will not thank you if charges such as this have not been pre-considered.

The box, Drainage – the basics, should serve as a useful aide memoire to drainage issues when you are out on a site inspection.

DRAINAGE – THE BASICS

The normal minimum drain diameters are:

- 100 mm for maximum 10 dwellings
- 150 mm for more than 10 residential units.

Clay pipes

Older drainage systems (Victorian or thereabouts) are most likely to comprise salt-glazed clayware pipes of 100 mm, 150 mm or 215 mm nominal bore diameters (i.e. 4 inch, 6 inch or 9 inch).

In many respects these pipes have stood the test of time but salt-glazed pipework suffers a number of problems.

For example, if not carefully bedded in a pea shingle or similar the pipes are prone to moving out of alignment and the joints gradually opening up with age so that they no longer remain watertight.

This can give rise to a number of problems:

- Paper and solids flushing down the drain may become attached to the angled edges at the pipe sockets where the pipes are no longer nicely aligned. This means a head of water is built up, and this increased pressure can cause more significant failure to joints elsewhere or to pipe connections into chambers and so on.

- Water seeping through defective joints may cause localised increased wetting to soil around the foundations. This can be a particular problem in clay soils where volume changes lead to heave or shrink, and subsidence or settlement in the property, or where the fine material in the soil can be washed out then settlement can occur.

- If the pipes are not at a suitable depth below ground level then the pipes themselves can become prone to fracturing and breakdown due to vehicle traffic from driveways, which were never intended for the volume or weight of modern vehicles.

Cast iron pipework

Sometimes cast iron pipework is used underground. This has considerable strength, but over a period of time can rust, and the rust expanding into the pipework can cause blockages, thinning of the pipe and eventual collapse/failure.

Pitch fibre pipework

Pitch fibre (bitumen-impregnated asbestos cement) pipework was commonly used in the 1940s, '50s and '60s.

The pipework was cheap but does not seem to have performed well or stood the test of time. The pipes are prone to deforming and collapse.

PROBLEMS – DRAINAGE

14.1 RELOCATING A SEWER

If you do need to relocate the sewer, in addition to the checks highlighted above, you will also have to:

- establish that there is sufficient invert depth for the new drain run to operate effectively
- consider appropriate treatment of any old drain runs which now become redundant, to prevent them becoming infested with vermin; pipes need to be either removed or properly and effectively stopped up.

Solution 1

When carrying out works next to older buildings it is common that a new drain run will end up being carried past the edge of an extension; and where the drain is lower than the foundations, appropriate care needs to be taken.

Where the edge of the trench is less than 1 m from the edge of the building main wall footing then the pipe has to be encased in concrete up to the level of the bottom of the footing.

Where the sewer pipe trench is more than 1 m from the edge of the main wall footing then the trench should be filled to the equivalent distance from the footing edge to the trench side less 150 mm.

The Building Regulations set out guidance for flow/gradient of different pipe capacities. For example, a typical 100-mm diameter pipe underground will need to be laid at between 1:10 and 1:70 gradient (the latter for up to seven appliances connected).

When planning the works, and after the drains have been inspected, you will need to give consideration to ongoing risks:

- Is the soil a very shrinkable heavy clay?
- Does the soil contain a high proportion of gravel or other fine material that could wash out and consolidate if there was a failure and leakage?
- Are there a lot of trees in the area which combined with a clay soil and subsequent drains failure might lead to risk of foundation damage?

If the drain run is a sectional clay pipe and you do not propose to replace it because the condition is more or less adequate you may wish to consider carrying out relining some critical 'at risk' sections, such as those running adjacent to trees to prevent tree root ingress in the future.

Resin-bonded polyester sleeve linings are comparatively straightforward to install, particularly in deep drains, which avoids digging and trenching.

Modern plastic drains are quite adaptable, and there are a variety of fittings such as flexible plastic couplings which can be connected onto existing drain runs using a large version of the conventional hosepipe clip, all reducing the amount of digging required – provided the rest of the system is up to specification.

Once complete, you will need to test the system, and if it is an older drain it may be more appropriate to use a water pressure test rather than an air test (which is notoriously difficult to apply).

Ensure the drain run has a proper soaking first so that any very minor leaks in the pipe joints are saturated and so is the soil surrounding it, to help provide an appropriate seal under working conditions.

COST SEQUENCE – Drain repairs/relocation

Assumed drain depth averaging 1 m below ground level. Drain assumed to be in pitch fibre or 100 mm diameter clayware.

Repair assumes a 4 m section to be excavated and repaired.

1. Excavate trench to expose defective drain.
2. Set aside spoil.
3. Carefully break out 4 m defective section of drain and excavate below soffit of pipe.
4. Fill the trench in granular fill, minimum depth 150 mm below the pipe soffit.
5. Install proprietary plastic foul drain pipe with flexible couplings where taken over to original pipe run and secure with stainless steel straps to pipe couplings. Bandflex™ or equivalent coupling.
6. Ensure pipe drains level with no back fall within the repaired section.
7. Fill trench min 150 mm above pipe crown with granular fill material maximum 10 mm size pea shingle. Consolidate.
8. Re-fill trench.
9. Assumed make good to ground surface; allow for reinstating of, say, concrete drive 150 mm thick across 4 m length of trench.
10. Remove all arisings and surplus material from site and cart away.
11. Costing assumes that the drain run can be isolated, there is no shared drain run or over pumping of neighbours' drains required during this operation.

Drain repairs – COST £540 (100 mm diameter); £650 (150 mm diameter)

14.2 SURFACE DRAINAGE

The drainage systems of many older properties are 'combined' – that is to say, both the foul and surface water drainage is run to the same system.

Many of these systems are now running at capacity, and have little or no scope to tackle the additional rainwater collected as a result of, say, the new roof surface of a large extension to the building (and hence the area drained from the roof, patio, paths and so on).

Solution

Depending on the size of the building extension, you may be able to put a case to the local authority that in fact there is no additional hard surfaced area being created – for example, where a patio is being removed and an extension put in its place.

However, if the extension is substantial with a large roof area to be drained, you should be looking at a soak away drainage system.

If things are tight, you could consider rainwater butts or grey water recycling as a form of attenuation to shore up the water where ground conditions have insufficient percolation to discharge the water.

14.3 SEPTIC TANKS

In rural properties it is common to find septic tank or cesspit systems. Many of these are of some considerable age, and are often rendered brick chambers. In my experience these rarely operate efficiently.

To make matters worse, with the number of modern appliances discharging into what might be a very aged drain system, failure is highly likely.

There is a very good chance that a completely new private drain installation will be required; and this will need to perform to a much higher standard than the original septic tank.

Also, if the works involve an extension to a property that has a septic tank, you need to put the Building Owner on notice that there may be considerable implications to carrying out extension works – well beyond the superficial building works envisaged.

Solution

If the system is failing, the Building Owner could be liable for any effluent and contamination discharged into the groundwater or nearby watercourses.

Guidance is set out in the Environment Agency publication *Prevention of Pollution Guidance for Performance Standards for Septic Tank Systems* (*www.publications.environment-agency.gov.uk*), and over recent years the standards have become increasingly robust. This publication includes advice about percolation testing and related issues.

It may be necessary to carry out chemical testing to establish the source of the leak, if discharge from the system cannot be obviously attributed to a defective septic system; alternatively you may need to consult a specialist contractor to investigate the performance and capacity of the system.

Testing is likely to involve specialist equipment, including a gas-monitoring rig and breathing equipment – all the more reason to call on specialist assistance!

Chapter 15
Plumbing and heating

Most of the information in relation to gas heating systems that you are likely to need can be found in the Gas Safety (Installation and Use) Regulations 1998.

The Regulations are comprehensive and even include comparatively minor gas fitting operations such as connecting a gas hob into the gas tap, as well as more complex operations such as fitting and commissioning gas fires and boilers.

KEY CONSIDERATIONS

◆ **The Institution of Electrical Engineers/ IET/Building Regulations and British Standards will apply to some electrical operations for plumbing in heating systems and vice versa.**

◆ **It is now a legal requirement that anyone installing or repairing gas fittings or appliances must be a CORGI-registered technician (*www.trustcorgi.com*).**

Note that, because there is a national shortage of qualified plumbing and heating engineers in Britain, some contractors may be tempted to consider wholesale replacement rather than a carefully detailed repair.

◆ **When specifying plumbing works it is well worthwhile going to the extra cost of including service valves/inline stop valves on the pipework. For example under tap tails so that taps can be properly isolated and new fittings installed if need be.**

Frequently bath taps and sometimes kitchen sink taps are pre-fitted to the sanitary ware before it is mounted in place. Consequently, if any repairs are needed later it is almost impossible to properly access all of the tap fittings to carry out a repair.

The presence of thoughtfully located stop valves means that repairs can be effected at leisure rather than necessitating a wholesale replacement of the tap, sink, bath and so on. It also reduces the need to chemically freeze-isolate sections of pipework (which is always an act of necessity rather than choice).

◆ **Always remember to check for leaks.**

◆ **Ensure that copper, galvanised steel and any other pipes are isolated from each other to prevent any preferential electrical charge building up which could erode the metal fittings.**

If you have a supervisory role, then take a tour of the site – before and after – the building works. You can use a proprietary listening stick to listen for the hissing/ringing sound of any water which might be escaping so that any new joints – or old plumbing – can be assessed for continuity.

◆ **Remember that when leaks are repaired, there may be increased pressure on other weak pipes or joints, which fail soon afterwards. Warn your client; sometimes complete replacement of old pipes is cheaper than a piecemeal repair in the long run.**

The box overleaf, Plumbing and heating – the basics, should serve as a useful aide memoire to plumbing and gas when you are out on a site inspection.

PLUMBING AND HEATING – THE BASICS

'Traditional' boilers

The Building Regulations no longer permit the installation of 'traditional' boilers, but there are plenty still in existence and you will encounter them in alteration and refurbishment projects. They are legal for continued use.

These boilers tend to be rather less efficient and with a greater NOx emission on combustion.

Although it may appear to be cheaper to repair than face replacement with one of the high-efficiency boiler options described below, this should only be considered where finances are extremely tight. Even then, there is the question of availability of parts; and the ongoing need for repairs. (An old boiler is likely to be one of the main 'issues' highlighted in the report that accompanies the Energy Performance Certificate, which will be included in the HIP.) If the client is on limited funds, or if there are a large number of boilers due for replacement within an estate/portfolio check for any grants available (*www.energysavingtrust. org.uk*).

Gas condensing boilers

A gas condensing boiler is a high-efficiency system which uses an additional heat exchanger element to remove heat energy from the exhaust gas from the boiler to provide additional heat to the system.

The boiler gets its name because the water vapour produced in the combustion process condenses back into liquid (this effect also helps to add to the heating output). This water is removed by means of an overflow type pipe, because it cannot be re-circulated in the system (it tends to be slightly acid).

The boiler is a very efficient system – and even more so when it is operating at maximum efficiency. Care should be taken to specify the correct size of boiler to suit the property, for example not installing a very large boiler in a comparatively small property, because it would be unlikely to reach peak efficiency.

The boiler also costs rather more than a 'traditional' gas boiler. However, the improved performance and lower fuel usage over the lifetime of the unit should defray some of the capital cost.

Combination boilers

Unlike a traditional system, the combination boiler does not heat water for subsequent storage in a hot cylinder in the airing cupboard; and there is no need for a cold-water tank or mains water domestic supply tank in the roof space.

A combi boiler runs off mains water pressure, and a special pressure cylinder is used to take up water expansion. For this type of boiler to generate hot water, the water is drawn through the system comparatively slowly, and the flow rate is therefore rather low when compared with a traditional pumped or gravity system.

This can sometimes lead to complaints from homeowners who do not fully appreciate how the system operates, especially if they have been used to the more old fashioned traditional system.

Careful selection is therefore required to optimise the flow rate for the boiler. This should be discussed with the installer beforehand – preferably before specifying, so that some accurate idea of cost and performance can be assessed.

When specifying boilers of all types, it may be useful to check the government-backed 'Boiler efficiency database' known as SEDBUK (*www.sedbuk.com*), which rates a wide range of boilers and is updated monthly.

The future

Other more efficient energy conservation systems may be available (though at the time of writing these may be more expensive systems and options).

Biomass boilers are currently receiving a lot of press attention. These rely on the heat generated by breaking down organic matter (which might range from anything on a farm manure heap to a more refined boiler system), and can prove extremely effective – although finding the fuel source, location to store it and so on means this type of heat supply is likely to be limited to rural locations or very specific easily serviced positions. (They require delivery of significant amounts of fuel, making inner city locations less suitable, and you would need to factor 'fuel miles' into the equation.) They have proved successful for local authority district heating systems, however.

An alternative to the biomass boiler is the micro-combined heat and power unit (micro-CHP), which is essentially a boiler that generates electricity as well as heat. Domestic-scale systems (which can run on either biomass or conventional fuel) are only just entering the marketplace, and are therefore currently considered 'experimental'.

Increasingly attractive are ground-source heat pumps, which rely on the temperature differential between the upper and lower strata of soil around a property. Systems vary greatly depending on soil types etc. – some might need to be buried at about 3 m; others at 8 m; but there are also systems that rely on a series of pipes set out as a network about 0.5 m or 1 m below the surface soil.

At the time of writing, the heat exchanger system would typically cost in the region of £8,000 to £12,000 but with very limited costs thereafter (essentially, servicing and gas pressure checking of the heat exchanger) apart from the electric pump used to circulate the hot water to radiators or domestic hot water system. This system operates with a compressor, so an electricity supply is still required.

Conceivably ground-source heat pumps will be the heating system for the future, but prices need to become more realistic. This type of plant is not always suited to high density developments because the pipe grids can impact on each other – within a terraced house setting for example.

The ideal situation is to achieve a building where the fabric is so energy efficient that it can be heated by the equivalent energy from a conventional lightbulb. There are then no moving parts to service, a much better built-in lifecycle cost and little subsequent energy expenditure. This is reflected in the highest level (level 6) of the Code for Sustainable Homes, which is of particular relevance to social housing projects.

Hopefully, when the penny drops we will be building highly efficient structures with no real need to heat them mechanically. Use of mass-based materials (brick or concrete?) may assist with heat retention and balancing the summer (cooling effect of the mass = no need for air-conditioning) with the heat retention and radiator effect of the mass material.

This is an area to watch for the future.

Plumbing materials

Vitreous ceramic continues to be the main choice for plumbing fittings (WCs and wash basins), and offers a number of advantages including comparative cheapness and ease of cleaning.

Plastic, copper vitreous coated metal pipes and compression fittings are all used for pipework.

You do need to be careful, however, in the selection of the product – cheapest is not always best!

Modern materials offer the advantage of speed of fitting, but are not always readily compatible with refurbishment of existing properties. It may be preferable to have only one style of fitting within a building, to assist future maintenance. There is, of course, a trade-off to be considered when considering new additions/alterations to an existing system.

Oil storage and bund wall/twin wall 'bunded' tanks

PPG3/4 (Prevention of Pollution Guidance) issued by the Environment Agency (*www.environment-agency. gov.uk*) provides simple advice for the prevention of pollution and is available on line and not repeated here. Bunding – placing some form of containment around storage tanks – is mandatory, but frequently omitted, and a significant liability could accrue should a leak occur.

PROBLEMS – PLUMBING AND HEATING

15.1 CASTING FAULTS IN SANITARY WARE

Sometimes, if not very carefully formed, the waste outlets and connection points can make the seating of pipes and pipe connectors, neoprene washers and the like extremely difficult. If the pipe fails to seat properly there is a temptation to over-tighten the thread on the connector, which can lead to the plastic pipe eventually shearing away.

Solution

It may be better to purchase a slightly more expensive product where quality is assured. Sometimes the more expensive products (including continuous non-jointed pipe runs for example) can save money in the long run.

15.2 LEAD PIPEWORK

When carrying out extension and alteration projects, look out for old lead plumbing under the floors – and sometimes also buried within the fabric of the walls beneath the plaster.

This could be 100 years old, and you can expect the lead pipework to be ready to fail, even if it has not already done so.

It is a false economy to retain it; and there are potential health risks.

Check also for earth bond continuity. It was not uncommon for the lead plumbing to be used to pick up earth bonding to the electrical system; and if the pipes are removed, new earth bonding will be needed.

Solution

It is usually fairly straightforward to cut off these pipes, but they will need draining.

● When carrying out extension works also watch out for galvanic corrosion risk from mixed materials.

Simple solutions save time and money
I remember a particularly good example of pipework, where a restaurant was being fitted in Brighton.

The building was extremely narrow at the frontage but had considerable depth from front to rear and it was a comparatively simple matter to use a continuous pipe run (pulled off a cable reel to draw the pipes through holes in the timber floor joists), taking the pipe runs from front to rear.

If a conventional 15 mm copper capillary jointed pipe had been used there would have been a significant amount of soldering and sweating of joints involved. This would, of course, also influence the addition on the contract sum.

15.3 EARTH BONDING

One of the most frequently omitted items seems to be the rating of circuit breakers on electric showers. The reason for this is not clear to me. It may be that plumbers are not always as up to date as they should be – although they should be complying with current electrical Regulations! Certainly in my experience a considerable number of showers are operating on either traditional cartridge fuses or wrongly rated RCDs with an obvious risk for health and safety. Bear in mind that the minimum rating shown in the electrical Regulations may be more relaxed than the breaker rating required by the appliance manufacturer.

15.4 BACKFLOW/SYPHONING

Without suitable checks in the system, water from one pipe can be drawn into another. Tainted water in a WC flush box or washing machine's flexible hose is not to be relished. Phenols in cheap hoses have a definite taste!

Solution

When specifying and checking works, it is important to ensure that double non-return valves have been installed, for example to washing machine plumbing/stop valves.

Although unlikely to be a huge problem, nevertheless the drinking water can quickly become contaminated by phenol plasticisers in the supply pipes to washing machines, dishwashers and the like and readily taint the taste of the water even if not a health risk.

Back-syphonage from the pipes can readily occur unless non-return valves are fitted.

15.5 RADIATOR SIZING

I can only imagine that 'slide-rule calculators' account for the fact that many a reception room will be fitted with a gas fire of some description; the radiator sizes could have been too small and frequently the gas fires have to be used to generate sufficient room heating rather than considered as an optional 'feature', or as a 'sales feature' in modern homes.

Solution

Once room sizes and volumes have been established, an early negotiation with the contractor should ensure that a more effective and efficient heating system can be installed from new rather than becoming a source of complaint on completion of the project.

Radiators should be accurately sized to suit room 'load' for maximum boiler efficiency.

Chapter 16
Electrics

Electrical wiring in dwellings is controlled through the Building Regulations (Approved Document P), which came into effect on 6 April 2006 (TSO; ISBN: 978 1 85946 225 6; download from *www.planning portal. gov.uk*).

Approved Document P provides the basic mechanism to bring electrical wiring work within the scope of the Building Regulations; and guidance in the form of Codes of Practice published by the IET (formerly the Institution of Electrical Engineers) and National Inspection Council for Electrical Installation Contractors (NICEIC) offer more comprehensive guidelines for the design of electrical systems and practical installation. Professional designers and installers are required to comply with the IET/ NICEIC/British Standards Codes of Practice. However, Approved Document P provides a 'condensed' code for householders, including a new formalised way for controlling electrical works, and discouraging the tendency to 'have a go DIY'.

This requirement was introduced in order to protect people from injury and death caused by incompetent do-it-yourself electrical work.

Some of the exemptions from Part P include:

- replacing outlets (power points/sockets, control switches, ceiling roses and so on), which does not comprise *actual re-wiring* of the installation (new fixed cabling)
- replacing the cable to a single circuit only where it has been damaged
- re-fixing or replacing enclosures to an existing installation (a component)
- providing mechanical protection to existing fixed installations – that is to say, sheathing or an improved conduit, for example

- improving or installing earth bonding (equi-potential bonding, e.g. between water pipes).

Some works are permitted outside of the kitchen or special locations, or where low voltage wiring is involved (e.g. telecoms rewiring).

KEY CONSIDERATIONS

◆ **Approved Document P affects dwellings only – residential properties.**

◆ **The Institution of Electrical Engineers/ IET/Building Regulations and British Standards will apply to some electrical operations for the plumbing of heating systems and vice versa.**

The scope of this particular book affects small building works as well as maintenance and repair.

◆ **Consequently, for practical purposes any *new* wiring works will need to comply with Part P and to be carried out and tested/ checked by a competent person with the appropriate copy of the British Standard 7671 Installation and Test Certificate supplied on completion of the works.**

You should ensure this requirement is incorporated within any specification for works, notwithstanding that it is a statutory requirement.

Approved Document P also summarises some 'older practice work that can be encountered in alteration work' which is well worth referring to; and it provides identification for the new harmonised electrical cable colour coding.

The colours of the live and neutral wires in electrical cables changed on 31 March 2006.

Red and black changed to brown and blue – the same as the wires in flexible leads to portable appliances.

♦ **Once an electrical installation has been completed (or indeed where one has been altered), then a BS 7671 check is required.**

For example, a plumber carrying out repair works to a hot water cylinder and immersion element would still be liable to establish and confirm that the part of the system being worked upon had been checked in accordance with the Regulations.

As with other aspects of repairs and maintenance, be sure you have a good grasp of the existing condition of wiring when preparing a specification. Points to note:

● Ensure cables are not covered by thermal insulation. This is a common issue where insulation has been upgraded, risking overheating of the cable. Unless thermally de-rated cable is used you need to ensure that there is adequate ventilation and air space around the cables. This can be achieved, for example, in the roof space by cleating them on battens clear of insulation material.

● Although cables should not be run down the cavity within cavity wall properties this is an occasional short cut. If any cavity wall insulation is being installed later or other works carried out, then there is a risk of electrocution if the wall is being drilled or broken apart in the course of the works. Check

for this; also check whether existing cavity wall insulation might cause the cable to overheat.

● Check that cables have not been run as shortcuts at angles across a wall and that the correct horizontal or vertical paths have been routed.

Keeping records

Maintaining a comprehensive data file is sensible, given that property owners may need to supply technical information to prospective buyers (particularly if the HIP expands to require some form of condition report).

In any case, it is always useful to have details of wiring and other electrical work for reference when maintenance or alterations are required.

In the case of commercial property, the data should be recorded in the Building Maintenance Manual (in the unlikely event it actually exists!), and a prudent surveyor will recommend such a file to the client. For example, cable runs need to be identified, and this information needs to be incorporated within the pre-tender health and safety file (CDM section).

The box, Electrics – the basics, should serve as a useful aide memoire to electrical work when you are out on a site inspection.

ELECTRICS – THE BASICS

Wiring colours

The colours of the live and neutral wires in electrical cables changed on 31 March 2006.

Red and black changed to brown and blue – the same as the wires in flexible leads to portable appliances.

Completion testing (BS 7671)

To summarise, very briefly, the main tests are:

1. **Continuity of the protective conductor** (the earth cable). This includes not only the main earth cable but also the 'equipotential bonding conductors', i.e. the earth straps around central heating or water pipes which might be used as a secondary protective circuit to ensure that, if these components should accidentally become live, they are earthed. (Stainless steel kitchen sinks are effectively included too.)
2. **Continuity of the main ring circuit conductors** – that is to say, both the live and neutral cables.
3. **Insulation resistance** – this is to establish if any of the plastic insulation sheathing has been stripped off and the live or neutral cables might be touching either each other or the earth circuit and are operating effectively.

4. **Polarity** – all switches, circuit breakers and fuses need to be correctly connected to the 'phase conductor' (the live cable).

Other tests may include:

● Earth electrode resistance checks. This is to establish that all of the earth cabling is of adequate capacity to earth the system (sometimes in an upgrade a newer more substantial supply and cable is installed but parts of an older and smaller earth cable are at risk of being left in situ). Where there is an earth electrode it must be capable of conducting any escaped current to earth.
● Earth fault loop impedance and functional testing of circuit breakers.

All of the test values need to be entered on a test certificate in accordance with British Standard 7671. This should be maintained – in the case of a commercial property – on the Building Maintenance and health and safety files; and in the case of a residential property within some form of building maintenance file.

Sources of information

In addition to Approved Document P, a very useful document is *Onsite Guide: BS 7671 (2001) 2004*, published by the IET, which is a commentary on the

16th Edition of the Wiring Regulations; note however that the *IEE Writing Regulations 17th Edition* was published in January 2008 (both documents are available via *www.iet.org*).

The *Onsite Guide* provides concise notes on specification for smaller properties – predominantly residential but could include commercial properties in some instances. Its small 'handbook' format allows quick reference to deem-to-satisfy design guides and standards for installation practice and should be on the bookshelf of any surveyor involved in building works – or in the car for convenient quick reference.

It will also be useful if you need to carry out some fairly basic checks of installation work (e.g. if you are acting as Contract Administration or Clerk of Works). For example, cable distances and positions, depth in plaster and so on can all be quickly checked and – if need be – demonstrated to the contractor where there are any shortcomings.

Chapter 17
Material matters

In a book of this kind it is not possible to provide comprehensive details of all materials used in construction. Instead, this chapter aims to draw your attention to some of the materials that are likely to raise questions during small building works.

CONCRETE

Concrete is one of the most important construction materials.

In recent years there have been some changes to the designation of concrete specifications. There have been various standards over the years, including those used by the Department of Transport, but the British Standard 5328 is likely to set the default for concrete specification in the future.

BS 5328 describes four options:

- **Designated mixes** – Effectively, these are concrete specifications set out in the Standard. Producers of these mixes must have satisfied external quality assurance for the design, performance and manufacture of the concrete specification. When using a designated mix the specifier is only responsible for choosing the correct designation for the final use of that concrete product.
- **Design mixes** – When using a design mix the specifier takes on the responsibility that it will meet the required performance for the intended use. Consequently it is important to ensure appropriate strength testing on site.
- **Prescribed mixes** – In this instance the end user is responsible for the performance of the concrete. The BS specification sets out the permitted materials that can be selected for the mix. Consequently the specifier needs a reasonably in-depth knowledge of how the concrete will perform in the specific situation and – by implication – requires familiarity in use for repeat specifications.
- **Standard mixes** – Appropriate for simple and repetitive specifying situations where the demands placed on the concrete are likely to be of a non-complex nature, under conditions which are frequently replicated and where reliability can reasonably be assured therefore. The standard mixes are comparatively simple specifications as a result, since there is unlikely to be any detailed site supervision or testing involved. (The standard mixes replace the former 'prescribed mixes' classified as 'C-numbers' based on concrete strength.)

Another option is to use 'nominal mixes', which are described by the mix proportions. This approach is suitable for simple site batching, but as there tends to be limited supervision involved with this type of specification, that can result in a more varied end product and very limited quality control involved.

- However, in my experience the quality is very likely to vary, so if there is the smallest chance that quality will become a critical factor, this would not be an appropriate method to use – although it is the most common one.

Examples of designated mixes include:

- Blinding and mass concrete fill – Gen 1
- Strip footings (in uncontaminated or non-aggressive soils) – Gen 3
- Trench fill foundations (non-aggressive soils) – Gen 3
- General applications such as oversite beneath suspended slabs or filling of wall cavities – Gen 2 or Gen 3 respectively.

- Ground supported floors in garages or houses in most instances – Gen 4; but for general industrial use choose a reinforced concrete – RC40.

There are a variety of designations for reinforced concrete for various exposure and wearing conditions; likewise for external paving, driveways and so on.

Foundations in sulfate-contaminated soil would vary between an FND 2 and FND 4 designation.

DELETERIOUS MATERIALS

'Deleterious' means hurtful, destructive, or poisonous. When applied to construction materials it tends to mean 'materials which might be harmful to health'; but it can equally mean materials that damage the building.

Always check with the client whether there is any risk of deleterious materials. It may also be appropriate to ask for information about site contamination – perhaps in the form of historical environment searches. In the absence of these it may be appropriate to recommend the client commission such a report – although for smaller domestic projects the risk may be comparatively minimal.

If land contamination is confirmed, then you will need the services of a geotechnical or other engineer to advise on remediation or containment strategies.

You will also need to have careful regard to your own professional indemnity insurance if a contaminative risk is identified (see Chapter 1).

Contamination in cities

If you carry out much work in cities you will not be surprised by the number of sites that have become contaminated over the last three or four centuries; but even in rural areas, contamination may be naturally occurring. For example, elevated levels of arsenic or cadmium are encountered well above the normal acceptable thresholds in some soil conditions in the West Country.

Disposal of contaminated materials and products may add considerably to disposal costs and thus to the overall cost of the contract.

The number of landfill sites has reduced dramatically, and you will need to plan disposal of any contaminated or deleterious arisings from the site. With fewer disposal sites, transport costs can add to the cost of tipping.

You will also need to ensure that any methodology considered is appropriate for working with potential risks or irritants:

- Various mineral fibres including spun mineral fibre, fibreglass – appropriate protection and breathing apparatus may be required. Consider using 'non-itch' recycled polyester insulation instead.
- Some solvent-based paints may require the use of respiratory protection/ventilation, particularly if working in enclosed areas.
- Timber treatments, subject to solvents used (many are now using water-based solvents).
- Formaldehyde-containing products (including chipboard and MDF) may be classed as an irritant or possibly a carcinogen – obtain an appropriate methods statement from the supplier, and/or negotiate with the contractor in advance to consider risks or look at specified alternative materials.

ASBESTOS

Asbestos is probably the most high profile 'deleterious material' of recent years.

The control limit is set at 0.1 fibres per cm^3 of air (measured over four hours), for work with all types of asbestos whether blue, brown or white.

The asbestos legislation primarily targets non-domestic properties although bear in mind that this also includes common areas to blocks of flats for example.

However, the Control of Asbestos at Work Regulations 2006 set a standard which really should be applied to domestic properties as well. And it is wise to bear in mind that almost any product used in the building industry over the last 80–100 years may well contain asbestos.

The new Regulations came into force at the end of 2006, and effectively consolidated the previous three Regulations.

You should certainly ensure that you are familiar with the HSE's Approved Code of Practice, *Working with materials containing asbestos* L 143, ISBN: 978 0 71766206 7 (*www.hsebooks.com*). (The ACoP *Management of asbestos in non-domestic premises* L127 was also revised in 2006.)

Despite some simplification and some minor relaxations within the Regulations, bear in mind that:

- there must be a responsible person in charge of the job – for assessing the risks; and to establish a suitable method of work to minimise exposure to risk
- anyone working with asbestos must have suitable training and understand the parameters of their job.

If you are working on non-domestic premises there should be an Asbestos Register already in place. Sadly, however, many clients do not seem to know their responsibilities, and you may need to educate them – advise on the appropriate level of asbestos survey to determine the level of rigour required in investigation, and the amount of detailed information required depending on the works proposed.

The results of an asbestos survey will determine the method of work, and also whether a licenced removal contractor is required to attend and make good before other operations can continue.

Note that work on textured coatings containing asbestos has been taken outside the licencing regime, because the risks are considered relatively slight. Nevertheless, you should still take care to ensure an appropriate method of work is deployed for textured coatings, plasters and so on.

Domestic asbestos risk

I recently heard a case where the whole downstairs of a house had to be gutted because the thick 1970s plasterwork was found to contain asbestos by workmen who were repairing ceilings following a flood from the upstairs bathroom.

The Health and Safety Executive publishes a comprehensive range of briefing sheets (*Asbestos Essentials task sheets*) providing advice, particularly useful where licenced works are not required (see *www.hse.gov.uk/asbestos/regulations.htm*).

LEAD

The Control of Lead at Work (CLAW) Regulations were published at the same time as the original Control of Asbestos at Work Regulations, and the CLAW Regulations (ISBN: 978 0 71762565 9) have now reached the third edition (*www.hsebooks.com*).

> **You should make sure you are familiar with the CLAW Regulations (keep a copy in the office), because some of the Regulations impact on the every day working environment.**

A common potential health hazard is old painted surfaces, where lead paint may be bonded to timber, and where a suitable method for removal of the paint finish needs to be considered.

WOOD WOOL

This was often used as a lightweight decking slab for flat roof structures, but is also found in lightweight partition walls, shuttering and various other applications. The material does not perform well if it becomes wet, when it turns to a soggy mass.

- A wet flat roof might not be safe to work on, or to walk on, and may require additional support, especially prior to roof repair works.

CALCIUM SILICATE BRICKWORK

Unlikely to be deleterious to human health (unless you drop it when you're not wearing safety boots) the brick is deleterious to buildings because it can be prone to shrinkage and requires careful location, specification of expansion joints and so on.

Generally this material has fallen out of favour, but it is often found on properties aged 25 years or more. The most common problem is one of inadequate expansion joints (see Chapter 9).

CALCIUM CHLORIDE CONCRETE/CEMENT ADDITIVE

This used to be used as an accelerator to improve curing times. It can cause accelerated concrete deterioration, particularly in damp conditions, with a subsequent risk of the reinforcing steel work corroding as well. Rarely specified in modern work.

HIGH ALUMINA CEMENT (HAC)

Typically used in the 1960s and '70s – again used to accelerate concrete curing – it can cause over-curing and deterioration to concrete.

In older concrete buildings it is sensible to know, prior to carrying out works, whether any accelerators or concrete additives have been used so that you can determine if there is any risk of deterioration to the structure. This might impact on demolitions, for example, if parts are less stable than expected; and it can impact on the life cycle of the building. (It would be pointless to design an extension to an office block with a 100-year lifespan if the main structure would only last a third of that time!)

MUNDIC

This is a quarried material usually found in Cornwall and other parts of the West Country. It was used to manufacture building blocks or as a concrete bulking agent.

If Mundic becomes damp it deteriorates. No longer used, it is sometimes encountered, particularly in West Country buildings from the 1950s and '60s.

If you work in the West Country you are likely to be aware of the problem; but if you don't and you are going to work there, then you need to be aware of it if you are dealing with older buildings.

Separate specialist advice is published on this including *The Mundic Problem: a guidance note* (2nd Edition), published by RICS (ISBN: 978 0 85406808 1).

OTHER RISKS

Here are a few of the other risks you might encounter when commissioning new works to older buildings or re-commissioning/combined extension and refurbishment works:

- **Water supply** – may require flushing through to remove debris from the system and prevent tap washers, valves and so on from seizing up due to grit or a build up of calcium deposits in the system.

  In hard water areas systems may be prone to reduced pipe temperatures if scale has built up, increasing risk of legionella.

  It is usual to purge the system at about 60 degrees in order to pasteurise the system as part of the commissioning process. If older parts of the infrastructure are to be retained in a building – particularly in public works – you need to ensure that the building services engineer has arranged for appropriate re-commissioning of the system.

- **Radon gas** – particularly in the West Country but many areas of the country have hot spots. The Health Protection Agency (which includes the former National Radiological Protection Board, NRPB) publishes a map identifying risk areas *The Indicative Atlas of Radon in England and Wales* (*www.hpa.org.uk/radiation*). Additional floor/damp membranes and ventilation to ground floor are usually required by Building Control in risk areas.

- **Methane and other gas from landfill sites** – may require venting off (or capture and incorporation within a district heating system).

- **Radiation from high voltage power lines** – subject to documents lodged in the NRPB archive of the Health Protection Agency, including *Advice on limiting exposure to electromagnetic fields (0–300 GHz)*, 2003, and related advisory statements and evidence.

- **Noise** (railway line or proximity to main roads) – may require special foundation design or acoustic control.

- **Use of reclaimed/recycled building materials** – may carry a risk of contamination and sourcing needs to be carefully considered.

- **Sea dredged aggregate** – Requires special specification for use of concrete mixes.

Chapter 18
Miscellaneous items

PAINTING AND DECORATING

By and large, decoration should be quite straightforward when dealing with modern construction and new build. However, by the very nature of this book, you are likely to be dealing with older properties. Therefore, before specifying decorations, you will need to cast aside any assumptions that spring to mind and look carefully at the situation that you are facing.

Although it is emphasised elsewhere in this book, it is well worth repeating – you need to ensure that you are combining compatible materials.

- Older properties might incorporate a lime-wash finish to external render, or you may find (occasionally) a property that still has distemper finishes – particularly on ceilings – and such surfaces do not take modern paint finishes well and are prone to flaking and blistering.
- Where distemper is present it is usually better to strip the finish entirely rather than to try and stabilise it, and this would of course add to the cost.
- Use of stabilisers once any old finishes have been stripped may, however, still be appropriate , e.g. use of PVA in a thin wash solution to control suction to old plaster finishes, for example, as well as bonding loose and desiccated surface material on the finish.

When carrying out maintenance or extension works there is a high likelihood that the building will still be occupied. You should therefore give careful consideration to the occupants. Are there babies or children in the house? Will it be occupied at all times during the day?

Use of modern low-odour and water-based paints may be appropriate in these situations, and in any case are increasingly preferred because there are no volatile solvents.

If the building is Listed, or in a conservation area, or there are wider conservation issues which need to be dealt with, you need to reflect on the implications.

You could carry out a simple test to check for lead; cheap and easy test kits are available from most builders' merchants. Applied to old paint finishes the test will help determine whether lead is present. This will help you to determine the most appropriate methods of repairing the surface. For example, stripping finishes by burning off would not be appropriate, in most cases, for lead paint finishes, and use of a chemical stripping agent would be preferred. You will also need to think about disposing of waste appropriately.

However, it is worth noting that it may be possible to continue to use lead paint on some Listed Buildings. If this is the case, you will need to check that the appropriate permissions have been obtained and that the CDM document has had proper regard to this.

Keep it clean, folks

Where buildings are being refurbished and large amounts of old wallpaper are being stripped out and plaster repairs are being completed prior to redecoration there is a peculiar tendency for large amounts of surplus mix to be flushed down the loo. It usually manages to proceed half way along the drain run to the property before solidifying in the drainpipe. The full extent of the problem usually only becomes apparent once the building is back in normal use!

All trades need to be aware that this is not an acceptable practice, and mixing buckets and paint kettles need to be properly cleaned out, with appropriate areas set aside for that purpose with waste knocked into the skip.

Any hazardous waste will need to be dealt with separately and appropriately.

Frankly, I have usually found it easier to ensure that the drains are scraped out prior to re-commission of the building, because despite all the best precautions, plaster or mortar mix, tiling grout and other nasties somehow still find their way into the drain run.

No nasty surprises please!

The fad for textured plaster finishes now seems to have diminished somewhat and there is a return to flat/plain plaster finishes. Consequently many refurbishment jobs require removal of textured plaster finishes and skimming over to create a smooth plaster finish.

- Asbestos was often used as binding agent or bulking agent in some of the textured plaster finishes, certainly into the 1980s; possibly later. Therefore it is essential to adopt an appropriate method of working when scrapping off the textured plaster. Wetting down the finish could be a minimum requirement to control dust.
- If the property is a commercial one, it is important to check the Asbestos Register, although this is no help for residential properties. If you think there is likely to be an asbestos risk then you have a duty to put appropriate precautions and even testing/removal in place. Certainly use of abrasive finishes to remove the textured plaster would not be appropriate in this instance.
- Sometimes with old buildings – for example, in kitchens – the plaster or paint finishes can be contaminated with oil-based finish. A variety of silicone-based stain-blocking agents are now available to skim over the finish. This will seal in the stain to provide a good base for further decoration, and so that the stain does not subsequent spoil the new finish.

Glossing over paint problems

An alternative – when in dire need – is to apply gloss paint over the area of stain, then undercoat over the gloss paint, followed by a build up of the appropriate decorative finish. Although this is not always successful, it could be your 'get out of jail free' card. Bear in mind, however, that the gloss paint means that the plaster will no longer have an absorbent surface; so this would not be an appropriate fix in a bathroom where large amounts of condensation are frequently absorbed into the wall to slowly dry out later.

When repairing plaster, it is important to ensure that the new plaster is compatible with the old, to prevent excessive shrinkage.

Some plasters may have a chemical reaction, so ensure that the appropriate trades are briefed in advance and if necessary there is a contingent sum in the specification, or the plaster specification has been determined in advance. Use of lime-based plasters would be appropriate internally in historic buildings, just as it would for external render or brick jointing.

BOUNDARIES – WALLS, FENCES, GATES AND RAILINGS

Many brick-built garden boundary walls end up becoming retaining walls by default, as earth levels are built up over time well above the original ground level.

If this becomes apparent and re-setting to the original ground levels is not feasible – for example perhaps because the next door neighbour's property has a higher ground level than the client's – then it may be appropriate to look at drilling drainage holes through the brick to relieve the weight of retained earth and water and some of the load on the wall. Of course, you need to check ownership of the walls first!

Ownership of fences and boundaries can become something of a hot potato, particularly in rural areas where stock fences were erected perhaps a metre or more inside the real boundary (and used to prevent animals pushing through the actual boundary line), but then become reinterpreted and the stock fence is adopted as the 'real' boundary.

Sometimes Party Wall issues impact on walls and fences. This does not mean that you necessarily have to choose the most obvious solution when constructing or repairing a boundary. For example, it may be possible to cantilever one end of a wall or fence to avoid the provisions of the Act impacting on a scheme.

Careful maintenance of records, checking of title registration documents and so on is appropriate if there is any doubt about works being carried out to or up to the boundaries, and it is important wherever possible to avoid a simple building job turning into a boundary dispute as well.

Bear in mind that any delays to the programme caused by such disputes can have a significant cost attached to them. To make matters worse, if the builders have allowed a particular schedule for the work, it may not be possible for them to come back and resume the same timetable once a dispute has been resolved. Pre-planning and communication pay off in this respect.

It is also important to ensure that the builder is quite clear about the ownership of the boundaries and any protection measures which might be needed in advance (see Chapter 7).

PROBLEMS – MISCELLANEOUS ITEMS

COST SEQUENCE – Fence post repair

Assume 5 no. timber fence posts are to be repaired at nominal 2 m centres across the run of the fence.

1. Provide temporary propping to existing fence posts as required.
2. Excavate pit adjacent to fence post between 750 mm and 1 m. Nominal pit diameters, say, 400 mm.
3. Fill base of pit with wet mix cement-rich concrete. Insert pre-cast concrete stub post and align with timber post. Back-fill post hole to ground level with wet mix concrete.
4. When concrete is set, drill through the timber posts (align drill bit through bolt holes in the concrete stub post). Insert engineering stud bolting nominally, say, M12.
5. Allow for timber plate to pack out between concrete post and timber post as required. Fit washer and bolt to each outer side of fence post and the stub post, and tighten up stud bolt across stud post and timber fence post. Saw off the end of the stud bolt and paint on rust inhibitor to exposed fresh metal.
6. Strike temporary supports.

Fence post repair – COST £225

18.1 EXPANSION CRACKS IN GARDEN AND BOUNDARY WALLS

Boundary walls are often constructed in considerable lengths and with little regard to expansion jointing requirements. If fissuring to the walls is caught at an early stage it is sometimes possible to cut in expansion joints at appropriate intervals without the need for additional substantive works to construct supporting piers or even re-build sections of the wall.

Solution

By carefully cutting a slot through the wall to open up the expansion joint to perhaps 10–15mm in width and inserting plastic-sleeved stainless steel expansion joint bars (something similar to wall ties) it is possible to tie together both panels of the wall and still accommodate some movement. This is relatively simple to do.

The plastic tube sleeves need to be carefully secured within the mortar joints and, where appropriate, an epoxy-modified cement mortar should provide good adhesion.

However, this technique may not be appropriate if significant jointing and re-pointing is carried out in a wall which was originally constructed with lime mortar, because this could cause water to be retained and result in subsequent frost action damage.

It is sensible to ensure that any slot cut providing a new expansion joint is appropriately filled with a fibre or compressible foam to prevent any stones falling in and preventing movement to the wall occurring and causing further cracking in the future.

COST SEQUENCE – Cutting-in expansion joint to freestanding half-brick-thick boundary wall

Assumed wall is of no greater height than 2 m.

1. Provide temporary support from raking shores or screw jacks as required.
2. Using rotary masonry saw, cut slot through existing expansion crack using battens nailed to face of wall to provide guidance.
3. Pass two cuts to open slot through wall, say, 15 mm in width.
4. Carefully chase out mortar bedding courses on each side of the expansion joint slot. Opposing slots are to be cut through the joints. Allow for, say, 4 evenly spread across the height of the wall.
5. Grout in using epoxy modified cement mortar plastic 4 no. sleeved stainless steel expansion joint ties. Grout into the centre of the thickness of the wall. Ensure face pointing is neatly completed in bucket handle finish on completion.
6. Insert compressible foam or fibre fill to expansion joint to prevent obstruction from entry of dirt and debris.
7. Clean away all arisings and remove temporary support.

Cutting in expansion joint to freestanding half brick thick boundary wall – COST £96

18.2 INADEQUATE SUPPORTING PIERS OR BOWING TO WALL

If the degree of bowing to the wall is relatively slight, then it should prove possible to either re-construct existing piers which are under-performing or to install what is, in effect, a new pier as a raking buttress.

You must check the wall first to assess the quality and condition of the mortar joint bonding.

If the wall can be noticeably rocked then it is unlikely that the mortar joints are sufficiently strong and it would be more appropriate to re-build the wall with adequate strengthening rather than risk collapse. This is particularly important in any location where young children might play beneath the wall or climb over it.

Solution

If the wall is reasonably firm but has started to distort with age or perhaps under the influence of tree roots, it should be possible to excavate around an existing pier or, if there is no pier, to construct a new foundation adjacent to the wall and build in a raking brick supporting pier to provide additional support.

Ensure that the raking pier drains properly, because frost will soon attack and damage any exposed brick surfaces.

The BRE Good Repair Guide no. 28 *Repairing brick and block freestanding walls* (2nd Edition) (*www.brebookshop.com*) is well worth reading, and recommends that half brick walls should probably be re-built if the distortion is 13 mm across the height of the wall; likewise 70 mm for a single brick wall or 100 mm distortion in a one-and-a-half brick wall. The guidance note does not explicitly state, but I assume that this is for walls that are 2 m high or less.

Choice of materials for boundaries

Although there is often pressure to apply the cheapest solution, the consequences of a collapsing brick wall do not bear thinking about. This problem frequently arises when properties come up for sale and are subject to a condition survey, and of course the vendors are frequently strapped for cash at that point, but the advice must come from a 'safety first' point of view regardless of the point of view, regardless of the financial consequences.

Remember, of course, that if a brick wall has to be demolished it may be a more cost-effective option to replace it with a timber post and panel fence or equivalent.

If you are involved with social housing you will find there is considerable pressure to use timber fence posts because of the sustainable renewable scoring under the EcoHomes rating for Housing Corporation grants (or the recently introduced Code for Sustainable Homes). While this is broadly to be encouraged, it is worth noting that timber fence posts have a fairly limited lifespan, and use of a timber fence set within concrete posts, which are properly secured in a concrete base, is probably more efficient in the long term, in my experience. (Trying to dig out and repair timber posts is generally a messy operation,

particularly once a garden or common areas have matured.) Installing (preferably) concrete gravel boards at the bottom of the fence will potentially extend the life of the fencing dramatically by reducing contact between the timber and damp ground.

If you must specify timber fence posts, these should be under 'Category A' of the British Standard 5589 where a target life of 40 years is specified. (Category B is for a target service life of 20 years.)

Timber quality for most domestic fences is unlikely to comply with most of the British Standard requirements, so check in advance. British Standard 1722 provides details of timber qualities for selection purposes (see Chapter 2), but there is always a risk of the timber rotting (even if a quality control process has been followed – there are no 100% guarantees!).

Assuming you are specifying a traditional wooden post fence with rails and boarding you will need to refer to British Standard 1722-7: 2006 which provides the main specification criteria.

If specifying railing enclosures, carefully consider whether you really want spikes on the top. These can have unforeseen implications – for example, how can window cleaners obtain access to the main elevations of the building, and is there a risk that they could fall onto railings?

COST SEQUENCE – Repair to garden boundary wall in brick

Construction of buttressing pier. Assumed wall height is 2 m.

1. Provide temporary support by raking screw jacks or timber buttresses to each side of the repair area as required.
2. Excavate around defective existing pier. Allow for excavation of pit, nominally 1 m by 1 m and depth nominally 0.5 m.
3. Pour concrete pad to nominal depth, say, 200 mm.
4. Construct solid brick raking buttress to height of, say, nominally 1.5 m and to maximum depth of new footing pad, say, 1 m back from face of wall. Face point new brick joints in cement-rich Portland mortar mix to improve moisture resistance and bucket handle joint face to assist with shedding water (unless works are executed in lime mortar).
5. Strike all temporary supports and clear away on completion of works and remove all arisings.

Repair to garden boundary wall in brick – COST £400

SITE WORKS

When looking at car parking areas, patios and other hard surface treatments around the main building there is something of a dilemma. In most cases you will be trying to achieve compliance with Approved Document M of the Building Regulations – either because the requirements apply directly to the project or simply due to good practise. Consequently you will be looking for level access between the paved/hard surface areas and the threshold of the building.

Give some thought in advance to how surface water will be discharged. Normally some form of drainage channel with a grating above is constructed at the abutment between the hard surface and the threshold to dispose of service water, but it would be sensible to ensure there is a drainage fall away from the main building.

How many dry rot cases in domestic properties start from the patio, either blocking off the under-floor air vents or draining water back (through the air vents?) towards the main building when this could easily have been avoided?

Some clients are determined to commission hard surfaces (even though gravel might be a suitable – and cheaper – alternative). If hard surfaces are unavoidable, then, ideally, some form of water collection and recycling should be employed. This would reduce run-off from the site, and may in turn lessen the flood risk (not just for your client, but for neighbours too). However, the cost of collection, re-use and compliance with the various water supply legal requirements may complicate this strategy. A case for further legislation and local Building Control interpretation if progress is to be made, I suspect!

Index